PLOUGHSHARES

Winter 2006–07 · Vol. 32, No. 4

GUEST EDITOR
Rosanna Warren

EDITOR
Don Lee

MANAGING EDITOR
Robert Arnold

POETRY EDITOR
David Daniel

ASSOCIATE FICTION EDITOR
Maryanne O'Hara

FOUNDING EDITOR
DeWitt Henry

FOUNDING PUBLISHER
Peter O'Malley

PLOUGHSHARES, a journal of new writing, is guest-edited serially by prominent writers who explore different and personal visions, aesthetics, and literary circles. PLOUGHSHARES is published in April, August, and December at Emerson College, 120 Boylston Street, Boston, MA 02116-4624. Telephone: (617) 824-8753. Web address: pshares.org.

ASSISTANT FICTION EDITOR: Jay Baron Nicorvo. EDITORIAL ASSISTANTS: Kat Setzer and Laura van den Berg. BOOKSHELF ADVISORS: Fred Leebron and Cate Marvin. PROOFREADER: Megan Weireter.

POETRY READERS: Kathleen Rooney, Autumn McClintock, Elisa Gabbert, Simeon Berry, Heather Madden, Julia Story, Chris Tonelli, Jennifer Kohl, Pepe Abola, Meredith Devney, Maria Halovanic, and Zachary Sifuentes. FICTION READERS: Laura van den Berg, Chris Helmuth, Sara Whittleton, Cam Terwilliger, Vanessa Carlisle, Kathleen Rooney, Simeon Berry, Eson Kim, Wendy Wunder, Hannah Bottomy, Elizabeth Browne, Marin Buschel, Leslie Busler, Leslie Cauldwell, James Charlesworth, Chip Cheek, Emily Ekle, Steve Himmer, Laura McCune-Poplin, Dan Medeiros, Matt Modica, Ashley Joseph O'Shaughnessy, Brenda Pike, Patricia Reed, Jason Roeder, Gregg Rosenblum, Asako Serizawa, Jim Scott, and August Hohenstein.

SUBSCRIPTIONS (ISSN 0048-4474): $24 for one year (3 issues), $46 for two years (6 issues); $27 a year for institutions. Add $12 a year for international ($10 for Canada).

UPCOMING: Spring 2007, a poetry and fiction issue edited by Edward Hirsch, will appear in April 2007. Fall 2007, a fiction issue edited by Andrea Barrett, will appear in August 2007.

SUBMISSIONS: Reading period is from August 1 to March 31 (postmark and online dates). All submissions sent from April to July are returned unread. Please see page 209 for editorial and submission policies.

Back-issue, classroom-adoption, and bulk orders may be placed directly through PLOUGHSHARES. Microfilms of back issues may be obtained from University Microfilms. PLOUGHSHARES is also available as CD-ROM and full-text products from EBSCO, H.W. Wilson, ProQuest, and the Gale Group. Indexed in M.L.A. Bibliography, American Humanities Index, Index of American Periodical Verse, Book Review Index. Full publisher's index is online at pshares.org. The views and opinions expressed in this journal are solely those of the authors. All rights for individual works revert to the authors upon publication. PLOUGHSHARES receives support from the National Endowment for the Arts and the Massachusetts Cultural Council.

Retail distribution by Ingram Periodicals and Bernhard DeBoer. Printed in the U.S.A. by Edwards Brothers.

© 2006 by Emerson College   ISBN 1-933058-05-6

CONTENTS

Winter 2006–07

Cover art:
Great Swamp South by
Heddi Siebel
Oil on wood, 18″ x 24″, 2004

Ploughshares Patrons

This nonprofit publication would not be possible without the
support of our readers and the generosity of the following
individuals and organizations. An additional list of
donor acknowledgements may be found on p. 211.

COUNCIL
William H. Berman
Denise and Mel Cohen
Robert E. Courtemanche
Jacqueline Liebergott
Fannette H. Sawyer Fund
Turow Foundation
Eugenia Gladstone Vogel
Marillyn Zacharis

PATRONS
Audrey Taylor Gonzalez
Drs. Jay and Mary Anne Jackson
Alice Munro
Joanne Randall, in memory of
James Randall

FRIENDS
Robert Hildreth
Jorie Hofstra
Tom Jenks and Carol Edgarian
Christopher and Colleen Palermo

ORGANIZATIONS
Emerson College
Houghton Mifflin
Massachusetts Cultural Council
National Endowment for the Arts

COUNCIL: $3,000 for two lifetime subscriptions and
acknowledgement in the journal for three years.
PATRON: $1,000 for a lifetime subscription and
acknowledgement in the journal for two years.
FRIEND: $500 for a lifetime subscription and
acknowledgement in the journal for one year.

ROSANNA WARREN

Introduction

"World is suddener than we fancy it," Louis MacNeice announced in his poem "Snow": "World is crazier and more of it than we think, / Incorrigibly plural..." So I felt, collecting the poems and stories for this issue of *Ploughshares*. The issue was like the great bay window in MacNeice's poem, with the writings as surprising, as "collateral and incompatible," as the snow and pink roses in "Snow."

The pieces I looked for dislocate ordinary language and ordinary vision, and relocate them in parables of sudden insight. The poems suggest stories while casting their song-spells; the stories tilt sentences and paragraphs into rhythmical sequences that formalize the words with which we think we are familiar from everyday speech, explanation, narration, excuse, prayer, and curse. I looked for work that would floodlight the true oddness of life in the crafted oddness of language.

A journal is a collective. That fact is both moving and revelatory. Writers work alone, but they work also in the light of centuries of the art that preceded them and gave them the forms in which they make their discoveries. And they work in the light—or is it the half-light?—cast by their contemporaries. An issue of a journal pitches a camp on a long caravan route. It is a provisional way station, and in the somewhat happenstance companionships and contiguities found there, one perceives a momentary pattern in the larger imaginative trade routes of a period.

The sense of the world as "suddener" and of art as, in part, collective teaches humility. Literature is ancient, and life's purposes outpace us: we are granted our glimpses.

> Love has its triumph and death has one,
> in time and the time beyond us.
> We have none.
>
> Only the sinking of stars. Silence and reflection.
> Yet the song beyond the dust
> will overcome our own.

So wrote Ingeborg Bachmann in "Songs in Flight" in Peter Filkins's lovely translation. Each true work has that humility, yet echoes, too, the song beyond the dust. That is what I listened for in the poems and stories gathered here. A note of triumph, also, sounds in a work of art well made. It has found a small order that will suffice until the next stab of vision, the next destruction. For it all must be begun again, over and over. In that perpetual beginning lies our hope, our private warrant against the world's insanities. The French poet René Char, deeply and responsibly engaged in military resistance to the Nazi occupation of France, composed two books of poems while he was hiding out with his men and fighting from the *maquis*. These books, *Seuls demeurent* and *Feuillets d'Hypnos*, were published only after the conclusion of the war in the volume *Fureur et mystère*. From his poem "Jeunesse" (Youth) I take one of the lines by which I live, and under whose protection I would like to place this issue of *Ploughshares: "Le chant finit l'exil."* Song puts an end to exile. Without such faith, why would we write?

And yet there are writers, rare ones, who work from a principled faithlessness, and so the question "why" is substantial and fertile, not rhetorical. A collection of poems and stories should provoke that real question, and leave the work of answering to go on in the mind of the reader. Whose every answer will be tested by the next poem, the next story. To keep us from sleepwalking. To keep us alive to one another.

ANNE ATIK

Anonymity

These strollers here under the arcades,
these anonymous passersby,
how would you greet them if met at parties
except in banter?
"Are you vegetarian? Virgo?
Rhesus? An alto?
Mesomorphic? Melancholic? Here's
someone sanguine. Phlegmatic?
Rheumatic? Optimist? You must be my-
opic. Blotto? Sit down. A zero? Now, now."

But no, they walk past each other,
step out each in his rectangle
that isolates one from another.
These strangers whose blood types may be incompatible
walk down together, unmindful of any danger;
in fact some of them stroll hand in hand.
They navigate, swarm,
free to not give their name,
through what only cities make possible,
flow and reflux as home.

Throngs of the meanwhile, the now, the soon,
of a lovely day in decline.

AMY BEEDER

Scarab Poetica

after J. Henri Fabre

O scribe, miner, pedestrian tracing the page,
try eating your house from the inside:

fruit-house, dung-house, make it your task
to bring forth flowers out of filth as you cage

the syllable, force the cadence; grind and pace
or mimic your betters under the argot surge—

Observe this recluse scarab waxing fat,
pulling grains of wheat from ordure,

matter from which the ovine's miracle
fourfold stomach could extract no fortune.

Utterance. Authority. Voice.
Denizens of dead cherry trees.

See how words rush in to fill the space?
Jewel thorax, trident, the dingy wing

in tatters but essentially complete;
and as there are forty-one classes of scavengers

you will find the line's elusive cast,
in shed skin or horn, the rind of years; as the larva

carves a mighty paunch from shit and yields
to no perfection, as the cotton bee

makes from its digestive dregs
an elegant casket; as *O. taurus* uncovers

always, the worm-dark apple's musty heart,
you will find the line to mend this season.

Nothing but words will fill the space:
So the Dung-beetle, sated with days, becomes legion.

Dawn

The sun didn't mind our handing the revolutions
back from earth to itself, so we could say
and believe once more, *It rose this morning.*
We allowed the horizon's gray
clouds to decide on a pale cerulean sky.
Many things we were taking back, giving

some away. The Mississippi could keep its rolling on.
Twittering was not from birds
but from the limbs. Howls at the intruder
sprang from the grass. The streets
would still deliver us where we wanted,
but we let them name themselves.

Sex floated free, too, where clouds
could sweep it clear, or make it rain down
to drench our clothes and hair. Where would freedom
take pause? Even death stepped back,
looked us over, and wondered. The sadness,
which once painted our houses, peeled away.

Hope hovered in the alley, tattering
its shirt, and getting up a likely story
to tell us on the porch while it stood
hat in hand. *Nobody wears hats anymore,*
we were about to say, already living
the future. We were glad to question

old and new. Ticker-tape parade, we thought,
return from the holidays and find home
celebrating its own sun-flattered beach.
Waves, wide horizons of open

ocean. Zero lot liners, how could we
resist the inspiration? Space and time

had stumbled within our grasp.

With Each Fresh Death the Soul Rediscovers Woe

from the world that called you Piñon not one voice is now not stopped
Piñon little pine nut sweet seed of the pine tree which is evergreen

Soul that discovered itself as it discovered the irreparable

breaking through ice to touch the rushing stream whose skin
breaking allowed darkness to swallow blondhaired Ramona

in 1944 age six high in the cold evergreen Sierras as you

age five luckily were elsewhere but forever after Soul there
failing to pull her for years of nights from the irreparable

Pas de Deux

A hairy hand with mouth and eyes,
    I would say, and was that scuttling,
that side-stepping jig, the furred upper legs

bent at the joint in *demi-plié,* was it
    scurry or whisk, romance or menace,
this tuft half-hid behind our garden shed door?

Her dragline ensnarls like a gossamer kiss
    to my thinking, she's thinking,
silk and white satin, a tryst in her nest.

How delicately woven an idea: spiraled,
    spoked, her hammock of lace spinneret
spun for a passing fancy. And does she prey

in the orb of her brain, waiting, as she does
    in shadow, for me, eight supple legs
tensile, poised—she's the size of a kitten.

Dusk has fallen, motionless. My breathing
    is two-four time. She's a brown fist
with fangs, the jumping genus if provoked.

Deep in her burrow of dark, I wonder
    what scintillant glint I am
beyond the net she was mending, beyond

the fading ground between us, fear
    and fear and nothing much
to say or do but gingerly back away.

Bitch Diary

Porco cane! Another day breaks
with a gunshot and a chorus
of yelping bloodhounds after boar.

I ache to join in, but stay quiet, loyal
dog-pig that I am. Pig-dog.
Purebred cur in a pen: *Sono io.*

The hunt's trained out of me.
Bark and growl, the baser instincts,
I renounced them long ago.

My tail springs up
like an erection
at the smell of animal,

but the chase
is forbidden. Always,
my inner *down girl!*

prevails. It never fails.
Not for me the bait of barnyard cats
and wild-goose foxes. I know

not to waste *my* nose
on vulgar game
or public sport.

I save myself
for the hidden
and vegetal.

I stalk the peculiar scent, wave
my tail like a secret banner when I catch the smell,
and follow the musk in silence

with a steady walk
to the still,
earthbound thing.

I paw the surface for a sign
—root-mold, fungus, spore—
then dig and claw

just to the tip of the tuber
till desire trumps dirt and
I lift the truffle.

I keep my panting discreet
and always deliver.
God, I am one good dog.

My mantra: Abhor blood.
Leave the surface to others;
dwell on the underworld.

Night Hunting

Because we wanted things the way they were
in our minds' black eyes we waited. The beaver
raising ripples in a vee behind his head
the thing we wanted. A weed is what might grow
where you don't want it; a dahlia could be a weed,
or love, or other notions. The heart can't choose
to find itself enchanted; the hand can't choose
to change the shape of water. How strange, to hope
to see the signs of motion, to make an end
to Peter's old refrain: *He'll be along, son of a bitch,*
and then you best be ready. So sure, and so sure
that when he shines the light the thing will show
along the other shore. What next? Well,
you've killed animals before. Invited here
for company in the cold night, and because
ever handy with rifles. What next is wait
and see, what next may be the lone report, the ever-
widening circles, blood-blossom, the spirit rising slow
like oily smoke above still waters. We wanted
a pond to look like a pond: standing poplars,
shallows unsullied, fish and frogs and salamanders.
The gleaming back of fur and fat may not belong,
or may: God of varmints, God of will, forgive us
our trespasses. We know precisely what we do.

Etruscan Song

No love like mine; no love; no love like mine
transformed a hotel room into a womb
and a womb into the child's cry;
love, no love, no love like mine.

Read in the dark, one hand on cock
Etruscan lore in my Etruscan book—
justice had another flavor there,
buried the son to punish the father.

Drove bolt-fast down the Merritt Parkway
one night, alone, singing *Please Bury Me;*
drove up the following afternoon
with a spade saying *dig me up, someone;*

dug up, found the sun so hot it burned;
craved the chocolate cool of dirt,
the pupa-life underground,
the coffin-dark of a dirt coffin.

So made, no love like mine, a boy;
turned dirt from chocolate to clay;
the clay became, one day, a cry,
and the cry turned night to day.

To Sleep

Then out of the darkness leapt a bare hand
that stroked my brow, "Come along, child;
stretch out your feet under the blanket.
Darkness will give you back, unremembering.
Do not be afraid." So I put down my book
and pushed like a finger through sheer silk,
the autobiographical part of me, the *am,*
snatched up to a different place, where I was
no longer my body but something more—
the compulsive, disorderly parts of me
in a state of equalization, everything sliding off—
war, suicide, love, poverty—as the rebellious,
mortal I, I, I lay, like a beetle irrigating a rose,
my red thoughts in a red shade all I was.

Alonement

Placed on the earth for this little moment
I wake today to entertain the world.
But, Lord, before first light only the clouds
my answerer, even to no question,
I stare outside, at the black broken universe
I cannot see: trees, clouds, birds, stones, fence, grass—
all the accouterments of worship on my eyes
and find myself, another Thomas come to doubt.
Oh, Peter, aren't you tired of being you?
At first light you will put your fingers out,
thrust them through the flesh dawn breaks on the glass,
the miraculous instantaneous.
Why, then, this darkness before everything
begins again? Everything without asking.

Sketches at the Hayden Rec Center

A solitary clock behind bars, floors
forbidden to street shoes, exit signs—

one, two, three, four: fine—& waxy cries
of boys, one mine, practicing their dribbling

& bank shots. My eyes closed, the volley
of Spaldings pounds like opening night

of *Operation Desert Storm,* or *Shield,* or
whatever war our Sonys dust up next...

Opening my eyes, I glimpse, time-lapse,
the pierced, lovely lips & eyebrows

of the future for these boys. Give them,
please, their share of nitrogen, oxygen,

& the less-than-one-percent of "other"
my son & I idled in, *en route* to Hayden,

in line at Walgreens's new drive-through,
watching a man cradle tulips to his van.

To study electricity, you need lights,
a Baghdad schoolteacher said on NPR—

after which we learned the hawk sees
eight times better than us. What gives

deadly eyesight to that beauty of a bird,
what gave those tulips an edgy splash

of apricot against the parking lot's
fresh tarmac & knolls of sod—is that

what can't simmer down in these boys?
Oh, they're trying, as the coach requires,

to stretch their fingers, rotate their necks.
When his whistle fires them down-court,

into the 30-second zone, they're home—
targeting each other, being themselves

targeted. At my son's age, I drilled
my blue & gray sharpshooters, & had

by heart the total killed & wounded
at Bull Run... A few more chest shots

& time's up. I peel my son off the pine
handholds bolted to cinder block walls;

navigate him toward the snack machine
for cheddar fries & Sprite; then to the car

where, sliding him into the back, I get
this burst of scent: part cheese-product,

part lemon-lime & sweat-tang in his hair;
& from the drugstore lot across the street

where a man hugged color like a pass
completed, the mix of damp earth & tar.

Ten Tankas

High noon in autumn
And another ovulation
Of sun on its way
Down the blue tube of the sky,
Then out the west through red leaves.

Newly awakened,
With first hairs turning silver,
She never conceived
Any leaves could look so red
Or heat her with their color.

One has to wonder
What she feels beside the sea
When the sun makes waves
Break out at noon in hives of light
And scintillating goose bumps.

From bed she can see
Mars in the west setting red
And knows her yearning,
As heavy bombs drop elsewhere,
Looks to some like luxury.

Like something selfish,
A privilege of safety
Removed from places
Birds catch fire and bleed in flight,
A child's hand lies in rubble.

And perhaps it is
Blasphemy against the black
Canyons slashed through streets,

Factories, squares, hospitals
To dream of lovers and flush.

But if so, then why,
She asks herself next morning
As she bathes and stares
At the leaves out the window,
Why would the ancients have paired

Mars with Venus?
How could one sit on his lap,
Hooking an ankle
Around a calf, and slide herself
Down his belligerence?

She slips on her shoes,
Closes the door, and tiptoes
The border between
Vehemence and violence.
Oh, how can she understand

This secret coupling?
As though finding an answer
To such a question
Would one day enable her
To plant a seed in the sun.

W. S. DI PIERO

Overlooking Lake Champlain

Rain spills leaf to leaf, rips some down
the chilly greenblack air, falls and falls
until it tamps October's ripened ground
that sponges up big plans. Sheet lightning
popped across the water and rubbed things raw.
The rain's tinny cymbal-brushing rushes
our nerves—we'll live how long to hear it?
Eighty today, Gracey on the back porch rocker
tells her daughter tidy, sewed-up thoughts
of killing extremities, what things they saw:
chairs, rugs, sheep, dogs, one cow,
bobbing in the torrent that November,
nineteen sixty-six, the Arno running
so swift it caught your breath, how she and the child
slogged alongside ancient Florentines
(books, cabinets, pots) saving what they could.

Our rain gives in to dull, fuzzy sun
while Fran details her plans, next month,
to go back, first time since the flood, insists
she weirdly remembers what wasn't yet there
to be seen: plaques and carved water lines
that mark church and palazzo and cut time
in place. Thoughtless excess runs through things,
death floods our nature before it even comes.
"You were this high" (pointing at the lake)
"but the water was *here*." Like a priestess, palms lifted
as if to gather and elevate us, the air, the instant,
wet leaves dropping while the rocker creaks
and she nods to nap in the expanding sun.

The Projected Man

I wander down rows of plastic magic—glowing
The boy comes home to a house too full of
skulls and x-ray specs squeezed in next to sneeze dust
decoupage and dead dreams, his mother nearly adrift
in genie bottles, fake ice where flies swim frozen,
on the dhurrie beige couch, worn down with being
arrested, ruled by resin, still as the half-hacked hands
worn, each hand beached on her belly like the dead
stacked nearby. I pass framed Charles Atlas ads, what
things they are. She has been waiting on him
would have been pressed, once, into the end pages
only to arrive, to reconnect, watch Dark Shadows
of *The Witching Hour,* maybe *House of Mystery,* all
together. They haven't done this in years.
sandwiched between other promises. THINK OF THAT MAN,
Waiting, what she's imagined has grown beyond
EVERYTHING YOU COULD BE. PUT ASIDE THE COMICS
her son. Maybe the afternoon will spill over,
AND BECOME WHAT EVERY GIRL PANTS AFTER. God,
she and the father rekindling what's become routine,
all the shit I remember. Myself, I could never get past the magic,
giving her a chance to forget the others,
even on my first "date." Then, now, what I think will impress
the lovers
only mystifies. That novelty nickel, the hollow
made of everything her life has ceased to be.
change I've brought to Debbie's today, makes my love
The son. He knows nothing of this.
laugh, yes, but *swoon* is what I'm after.
A girl named Laura has just become his
Madness, I know, but still I show her its profile, its single
world, and today she'll be at her friend's.

side, the hole in the eye that, when squeezed,
        Asking only to go back out, he confronts
drenches the unsuspecting.
        eyes that seem suddenly to collapse, frail stars
In this case, her.
        grown too vast. Gravity guides her nod.
Anger. Confusion. She grabs the magic
        Maybe wanting, what drives them both,
away from me. "Heads," she says—there is only
        what pedals a boy onto his bike, a mother into
heads—and tosses my mistake away. I swear
        her Monte Carlo, spins
away. It never comes down. So here I am still looking for
        her down the road, toward cities,
another one, another forever
        away from the plain and
hollow novelty
        out of their lives.
I can't forget.

Anywhere Elsewhere

How anyone is happy in this country
I don't know. Any way you turn
there is an edge, and everyone
cocks a wind-burned hand over
the brow to look out under it.
The water flings petticoats of foam
against wolf-headed rocks, and
multicolored boats moored
among others to the weathered
pier bob dumb as soldiers.
We live on what's beneath us.
Dark snake-like birds curl into
the water, rise like rose blooms
floated in bowls. And every day
the riven, mended nets go trolling.
A far cry from my unforgotten fields.
How is it, then, the boat lamps
and the buoy bells dislocate me?—
aching not for home, for something
I can't name. As if I could be half-
another, as if I've lived someplace
I never will. Winter brought greenish
bergs to the harbor, floes composed
of further waters. And the strange
white crows here rode them.
A mustached woman poured
scalding coffee on the feet of one
to free it from the scalloped ice
night layered on the sand.
It screamed as my lost brother
does in dreams, with a creature's
anguished hatred. Next morning,
it lay in the wheat-colored grass,

half-eaten by dogs. Here, shells
resembling army helmets wash
ashore, and cataracted eyes of horses.
The town creaks, the seaward shingles
of the dry-faced widows' houses
loosen like teeth. A squall will snap
a mast in half clean as a bone.
Are we not shipwrecked?
The gravid sea holds nothing
for us—but how we squint out
over it, waiting for another sun,
for someone else's blessed hour.

Winter Park

What matters is how you
disagree
with me, not the smooth surfaces
of your appeasements.

Let snow melt off the statues,
parks come and go like seasons.
See the park in snow
see my hands rough from snow
fingers red and stiff
and remember the past
when they begin to thaw

filling with pain
they will live again,
the excitement howling inside
like a park on fire
a burst of flame
displacing the shapes of snow.

What matters is how you agree
with me
not the smooth surfaces
of your appeasement.

To My Brother at His Funeral

Flying over many states,
driving through many streets,
I come to The Chapel in the Pines,
where a film of your life shows our trunks
bunched in at the crotch as we take turns
burying each other in the sands of Far Rockaway,
each standing by a mound, like archeologists
discovering tombs, tombs of their own making.

At your plot overlooking the studios
you wanted sprinkled with your ashes,
a green box, like the one holding my valuables,
is passed among the mourners, while a workman
jumps into the grave. Frightened by imagining
you as ash, I recall your body at the beach.
The minister announces, "David's brother will read Kiddish."
I correct him, and make my own mistakes.

Divided, we built a memory-bridge out of
what we saw from the identical bedroom window,
like two scholars of an illuminated manuscript
that is fading under their very eyes,
and they the only ones left to read it—
Vic's barbershop pole scrolling up, or scrolling down,
"Gabilla's Kinishes" in Hebraicized lettering on the delivery truck,
Goozhie and Lovie, like lab partners, gauging the handicaps at
    Kramer's candy store.

Oyster Money

Stabbed by the heron's shadow
as the bird planed above me on these flats,
I am back in Taylorville, 1958,
scratching the low-tide mud with Linc
and his father, the Kaiser. "No future
in oysters, boy." The old man's advising
one or both of us to stay in school
or else enlist in the Navy: "Three hots
and a cot from Uncle Sammy, finest kind,"
he says. "No future in oysters." This
from a childhood of them nightly
staring back from his plate, Black Friday
to Pearl Harbor, and a lifetime
of digging, bagging, hauling, shucking,
and selling, but not eating any more ever,
not on a half-shell or stewed, fried,
and damn sure not Rockefellered.
When Linc and I cut out to deliver
to restaurants over on 6A and 28,
the old woodie's riding low with bushels
and so rusty that just the brine smell
could cause it to pass over into dust
after years of wet burlap and waiting
by salt water. On 6A the tourist cars
are wondering why a Bud can seems
to fall occasionally out of the sky.
When I take the wheel outside Lucky Jim's
and head for the Oceanside Inn, Linc draws
his guitar from behind the seat
and picks off "Under the Double Eagle"
and "Back Street Affair," and worries out loud
between tunes that we won't get home
in time to distract his father. "That man

can be some foolish with a dollar,
particularly a roll of oyster money
that could choke a horse." Which doesn't
prevent us from tilting another one
or two at a couple of taps where they find
our folded floppy hip boots colorful. We take
the side roads home, avoiding the cops
of three towns, and are too late. Because now
Kaiser's got friends, plus a Mr. Kenneth straw hat
with butterflies and little Bud cans on it,
and a yellow shirt plastered with Diamond Head
and upside-down palm trees, and not just
any friends but Boggsy, Billy Morna,
Captain Teabag, a gallery of harborside
slouches leaning on Jazz Garters's DeSoto,
its red and black matching their Carling cans.
The look on Linc's face is conveying
another winter under tarpaper. Kaiser
can't look at his boy. I can see he knows
what kind of friends he has, but he's
seeing the state road, too, empty ten months
of the year, and closing time,
and walking home from Mahar's in the rain.

Fig

Color of a two-day new bruise,

pored and faintly fuzzed like the pad
of a dog's paw.

Skin so thin faucet water risks
rubbing through to moony fruit,

the shape and pitless-centered
weight of testes.

No stone, too malleable
so, not a drupe.

Dropped, it wobbles
to find plumb center, comes
to rest on star-shaped navel,

the smell of chemical, venom,
jaw-locking tannin.

Squeezed from the stem, bursts
to coral crop of seeds,

to sea-tentacled center.

First fruit and God-prescribed
diet, eat four before
they start to taste

                              like echoes
of other fruit: peach-sweet, cucumber-
clean, musked honey of plum

sucked by a bat who wraps
dusk-colored wings
and throbs till the casing's
scraped clean,

discarded skin
of a boxing glove.

LINDA GREGERSON

Make-Falcon

Frederick II of Hohenstaufen, The Art of Falconry

1.

Of the oil gland ... Of the down ...
        Of the numbers and arrangement
of feathers in the wing ... I have seen
        on the plains of Apulia

how the birds in earliest spring were weak
        and scarcely able to fly.
Of the avian nostrils and mandibles ... Of
        the regular sequence of molt ...

Aristotle, apt to credit hearsay where
        experiment alone
can be relied upon, was wrong about
        the migrant column. Concerning

the methods of capture ... the jesses ...
        The swivel, the hood, the falcon's bell ...

2.

The finest of them—here I mean
        for swiftness, strength,

audacity, and stamina—are brooded
        on the Hyperborean cliffs (an island
chiefly made of ice). And I
        am told but have not ascertained

the farther from the sea they nest,
        the nobler will be the offspring.

37

3.

Triangular needles are not to be used. The room

to be darkened, the bird
        held close in the hands of the assistant,
linen thread. By no means pierce
            the *membrana nictitans,* lying between

the eyeball and the outermost
        tissue, nor place the suture, lest it tear,
too near the edge. To seel,
        from *cilium,* lower lid,

which makes her more compliant to the falconer's
        will but also (I have
seen this in the lesser birds as well) more bold
        in flight. The senses

to be trained in isolation: taste,
        then touch, then hearing (so
the bars of a song she will evermore link to
        food), and then the sight restored,

in order that the falcon may
        be partly weaned or disengaged from that
which comes by nature.
            The falconer's purse or

carneria, owing
        to the meat it holds ...
The carrier's arm ... the gauntlet ... the horse ...
            They greatly dislike the human face.

4.

If you ask why the train is made of a hare,
        you must know no other flight

more resembles
> the flight at a crane than that

the falcon learns in pursuit of a hare
> nor is more beautiful.
>> Make-falcon: meaning
>>> the one who is willing

to fly in a cast with another less
> expert (the seasons
best suited ... the weather ... the hours ...)
> and by example teach.

5.

The removal of dogs, which praise
> will better effect than will the harshest
threats, from the prey. Their reward.
>> You must open

the breast and extract the organ that moves
> by itself, which is to say, the heart,
and let the falcon feed.
> The sultan

has sent me a fine machine combining
> the motions of sun and moon,
and Giacomo makes a poem of fourteen
> lines. The music is very good,

I think. (Of those who refuse to come to the lure ... Of
> shirkers ... Of bating ...)
But give me the falcon for art.

JEFF HARDIN

On the Eve of a New Millennium

Drunk off his can and pissed at the ruse of another day,
backache a bum rap and woodpile shrunk to kindling,
the old man stood at the kitchen sink and stared out
at his neighbor's cow. *What a filthy beast,* he thought.
What a stinking, cud-chewing, gas-spewing waste of a field.
And then, because what else should happen on a day as dull
as this one, what better way to stun the silence out of all
it cannot say, he stumbled through the ashen rooms to find
his gun. The front room table spilled its stack of magazines
and pens. He was not a man who cared one whit for what
you might have thought of him. He spat cruel words and mocked
your God and cheered the buzzards dropped to feed on roadkill.
What was all this talk about a new millennium to him?
Weren't the evening and sun the same as always, and nowhere?
Even drunk, he didn't miss, and the cow tumbled down
dead-weight and draining blood, and the good earth shook
on its foundation, knocked off its axis for a visible second,
the good earth clutched at the blood, drug it down, down,
and the neighbor boys hid in the back of their closets.
Here was a stretch of road a man like him could tuck himself
back down and not have to answer to a soul, least of all
some dimwit codger whose cow would stare him straight in the eye.
And then what happened, you'd like to know, as if stories
have endings that conclude or explain, as if stories heal loss,
stop time, weep light, speak truth, change lives, dream souls.
He tumbled himself into his truck, took off toward town
slinging gravel and missing the ditch, his arm out the window
conducting last light on the maples and shagbark hickories,
damning them all to hell, even the burnt stalks of corn
and the useless rail fence and the pigs caked with mud
lost somewhere he was tired of looking, and those bible verses
learned fifty years ago of the good soil and the bad soil,
and it took just a mile before he saw a car coming, and aimed.

J. BOYER

The Night Mechanic

A Romance Novel in Ten Short Chapters

Chapter One

One day—taken by the lilt of his wrists and the most beautiful hands she had ever seen on a man—she impetuously threw in her lot with a deaf and dumb mechanic who'd been deaf and dumb from birth. She fell in love as she was watching him sign, after meeting him in a garage one day, and after this they lived together in poverty in a succession of rented cottages in the small and still smaller villages of northwestern Scotland until finally they came to light near Northrup's Weir, only for her to discover in a state of generally failing health that her health wasn't failing at all, she was dying of one of those vague but specific diseases for which medicine knows no cure.

So there they were, our dying woman and her deaf and dumb mechanic, in a cottage near Northrup's Weir, and a pretty poor cottage at that.

Chapter Two

There's never one unhappy person in a troubled relationship, always two, and never is this more the case than when one of the two is dying. She saw to that. She spent her days toward the end writing him sad little love notes and fashioning awful little dolls from bits of wool and twists of paper which she made him promise he would bury beside her. When he brought her a fork to eat with, she bent it: Forks were for those with their health. It was almost as if she were angry that he might survive her, for she cast herself now in the role of someone trying to slip over the edge of a raft so as not to be a burden in a cold and choppy sea, which was to say that no matter how fast he rowed, it could never be fast enough to save her, and Frank was meant to see this. Measuring out her dosages before leaving one night for work, he secreted the wish that she either recover miraculously before he returned or drown in her sea and be done with it.

Chapter Three

There was no reason to suppose that he could help her save her life by embracing his own, yet he felt as if he might, and with a burst of energy he began this procedure as if it could all be done by the sweat of his brow. After scrubbing the cottage from top to bottom and replacing a broken drain spout, he gave it two coats of paint, and with that out of the way, he borrowed books from the library. He read a chapter a day for a week. He bought a new pair of trousers and drew up a list of a hundred and forty-seven things that might make him more appealing, some of them purely ridiculous, such as "MORE TALK" or "PUT A TWINKLE IN YOUR EYE." He tried to think of other things as well, but he was out of his depth, and when the rest of the month went by without a sign of her improving, he began to suspect that the efforts he was expending were of complete indifference anyway and he'd been foolishly wasting his time.

Chapter Four

To conceal the taste of her fate, Frank, our mechanic, regularly served her tea in bed braced with teaspoons of whiskey when he brought her her medicines, and showered them both with the odd little gifts of someone unfamiliar with how money can be spent, thinking, So much for economy, using the last of what they'd thought of as their savings on matching little things like silver-plated pencils and fur-collared coats.

Her sickness had spread through their rooms, edging him out, as a sickness sometimes does when there's no real hope for recovery, and now it was only before their listless kitchen heater that he felt fully in possession of himself or anything else, and the graying sky outside did nothing to increase his cheerfulness one morning when she called for a pot of tea. He offered biscuits as well, for her strength. He counted out two out of habit, though there was money for more. Putting the kettle on to boil, he took a glass from the cabinet, poured himself—measured himself, more properly—a full three inches of whiskey, drank it straight down, then drank from the bottle itself, burning his gums and his tongue. That they'd lived hand to mouth for so long when there was money available began to seem like something she'd done to betray him, rather than a fate they had suffered in common.

She refused the biscuits he served on a tray. Too delicate now for cake, she asked him to boil her an egg instead. It took forever to fix it. He pointed toward the book she'd been reading, meaning, Is it a love story? "It might be," she answered, "if someone would die." Later, holding her hand in both of his own, he explained the delay.

Chapter Five

The garage where he worked had the flyblown air of a business that was going down, and Cal, its owner, who liked to date the milestones of his life by the few times he'd shown a profit, "Let me see now, I've had two operations and three kids since that year we were flush with cash," was always going on about having to fold his tent and move on if things didn't pick up very soon, but there was no more chance of that than of Cal sprouting wings. He'd been saying he was going broke for more than thirty years. To make ends meet, Cal kept the garage open round the clock, working sixteen hours out of twenty-four, seven days a week. The less money the Scottish have, the less inclined we are to set a table and spend it on food, so his wife, a sharp-featured woman with frail bluish teeth, brought him his meals there, generally white bread and margarine, stewed beef, sugared tea, and potatoes, whether this was breakfast, lunch, or dinner, so, reasonably enough, there was generally a whiff of meat fat in the office, rather than of rubber, petrol, and lubricants. It never quite smelled right to Frank, a mechanic. There shouldn't have been air you could taste. You walked into a garage, and the smells should have hit you in the face with a smack. It never quite felt right, either. Working for Cal hadn't felt right since the day he went to a box of secondhand distributors and found instead of distributors a pudding basin, three unopened bottles of Worcester sauce, and two dirty cups. Nevertheless, the garage was as near as Frank had to a lifeline at the moment, helping to keep him afloat.

Chapter Six

Fridays were slow as a rule. Cal was generally out of tobacco toward the end of each week, but lit or not, Frank expected each Friday to get to the door and find on the other side the sunken cheeks of Cal's childish face as Cal drew on one or another of his ragged briar pipes, turning the pages of his racing final as if paring the skin from a yellowish large potato. The only thing out of the ordinary was that as Frank arrived for work that Friday evening, one of the locals was unfurling an air hose after fixing a flat on his bicycle using a puncture repair kit. Frank waved as he opened the door. "Quite all right, thanks," answered the cyclist. "Take care with your fine coat there. Don't want it getting greasy. Dismal night to be on your bike." Frank's coat felt warmer for being called fine. The cyclist with grizzled hair and a clipped mustache had been a lower-grade civil official who had recently come down in the world and moved to Northrup's Weir, where he'd opened a business. Frank didn't know his first name. Jencks was his last. He had something to do with insurance. Normally he would have ignored the man, and he was glad that he didn't, since his coat felt better for being called fine.

Frank's first chore of the shift was to empty a trash barrel. Work orders were listed in the sequence they'd arrived in, multi-colored chalks on a green slate board with a corrugated gutter. The air inside the shop was chalky. Almost like snow, the chalk in the air was firm and powdery, and it covered the hard wooden chair. He put on fingerless gloves. A thin curtain of pipe smoke dulled the glass of the window that faced out toward the pump.

About work, Frank was preciously aware of something the rest of us take for granted, namely, that there's a point at which the work momentarily vanishes, you're completely at one with yourself, and there seems to be no possibility at all for error, so he looked forward to tinkering with the cars he'd find in need of his service that evening. He found the same kind of selfless precision in working with his hands that others might find in working with lace.

The first of the work orders was for a Jeep Wagoneer that was out in a bay with a lift. Someone had put so much sawdust in the transmission to keep it running that its transmission fluid was clogged with fruity-smelling solids. The bay was locked. He opened it with a key.

The Wagoneer was an ancient Hydra-Matic that had been designed as though it would never need repair, not even minor standard maintenance, for everything was difficult to reach or took seven steps to do. The transmission didn't even have a drain plug. To change the transmission fluid and filter he would have to loosen the pan and allow the fluid to spill out over the top of the transmission pan, which meant the fluid spilt over everything. The transmission pan was held in place by two attaching screws at each corner. The first thing Frank had to do was to put a drain pan down on the ground under the corner he started with. He loosened the two attaching screws, a little bit for this one, then a little bit for the next. What he was trying to do was to loosen all the screws of the transmission pan so that the fluid would drain from the corner where the drain pan was waiting to catch it. When most of the fluid was drained in this way, he had to push up on the transmission pan with one hand, take out all the screws with the other, then lower the transmission pan with both hands, slide out from beneath the chassis, and dump what was left of the fluid that had settled near the bottom before he could clean and dry it.

He was cleaning the pan, standing over a drain with a long red tube of India rubber in one hand and the pan in the other, when the car's owners arrived, a couple, Frank assumed. The man said to the girl, "Why won't you use a proper car instead of this junker?"

Dyed a bright polymer green, the girl's hair was buzz cut into a rectangle half an inch high, and she brushed it with her fingers as she spoke, as if brushing this away. "Do you know what I make, working in a scent shop?"

Chapter Seven

That was the night it happened. A Friday. Returning from work, he found her dead in their cottage. She had died that night in her sleep, not the girl who had looked to Frank as if she'd strayed from the mother ship, but the woman who Frank had once loved. Our mechanic beat himself about the head and shoulders—figuratively speaking—for the better part of that morning for having gone off to work and left her to die by herself in the middle of nowhere. Deciding shortly after the lunch hour that it was time to say goodbye, he stood on the threshold of the room where she lay. He pushed open the door. Entering the room, he realized the coverlet on his side of the bed was neatly turned back at an angle as if he'd been expected to spend the night there. The thought gave him goose flesh. Seeing her lying there dead, he felt the same way he'd felt once as a child when he'd seen a naked man on a snowy cold day: It had made Frank glad for his clothes. He closed their bedroom door behind him. He shut it tight. No one was there to tell Frank that he couldn't go into the room again, of course, yet he had the feeling it would be wrong to do so. With his back to the door, he wanted so badly to scream at the unfairness of it all, and his limbs were suddenly leaden at the thought that he couldn't. To keep feeling in his toes as he stood there, he developed an exercise on the spot whereby he lifted his heels from the ground so that he was supported by the balls of his feet. Later he notified the authorities to come for her body.

Chapter Eight

Grief's a mysterious agent. We find nothing so surprising as the ease with which death can rob of us of those we've loved, no thought more absurd upon losing someone we've loved than the thought that we'll never see them again, and for Frank she was even more real in death than she had been while she was dying. Once her body had been removed, death, her death, at least, took on tangible dimensions, height, weight, mass, physical characteristics, where once it had stood just beyond the scope of any lantern they'd shone upon it, and he treated it as such for the rest of the afternoon. As if she were just away on a trip, her death became her absence.

Frank arrived for work that night just as the sun was setting, and his employer was hopping up and down in agony after walloping himself on the forefinger with an oily ball-peen hammer. Frank was soon left alone. After slipping on a pair of overalls he found hanging behind the door, he emptied the trash, then spent the shift without so much as the hint of a customer.

Cal had sawed off the arms of the chair in the belief that arms made a chair more comfortable. A man might not leave a comfortable chair. Arms or no, Frank stayed in that chair all night, leaving it once to put out the trash and a second time at dawn to use the men's lav. Taking the key ring from the wall, he went around to the side of the building at the end of his shift, where he washed his face with a fist of paper towels. To make sure no one slipped the key in their pocket and drove off by mistake, Cal had put a counterweight from a pair of Calvinist velveteen curtains on a huge metal ring. He would have done this for the ladies' as well, but women, reasoned Cal, wore dresses and skirts, not trousers and coats. Men were the ones with real pockets.

Chapter Nine

Cal came to relieve him at the usual time. "So?" asked Cal. Opening the cash drawer, he continued, "Nothing new? Things were more or less like always, then? You didn't burn down the place. It's still here. Poor comfort."

Shortly thereafter, brushing aside the wing of a crawling insect, Cal took a clipboard of parts orders from beneath a pipe rack that held three of his favorite sandblasted briars and inked in the blocks near the bottom. Frank watched as he did this. Cal had to labor to get the forms right. Like all artisans with permanently dirty hands, Cal had a peculiarly delicate manner of handling things, particularly all things confusing, as if he feared he might break them, the way a small-boned woman might handle a bird or a starving man might pick up a crumb, and, as consequence, he had to labor over this more than most of us might. When a car pulled up at the pump, he said to Frank, "Her. It's her again. The pump, Frank. If it's not too much trouble."

The driver was giddy. She'd been drinking. Wondering to himself if the woman would make it home alive in the condition she was in, wondering if he would find her on his way home in a ditch, her windscreen a cobweb of shattered glass, and her son's eyes as lifeless in death as a pair of children's marbles, Frank filled the tank of her foreign sedan while the woman went inside to place a call to her girlfriend. Frank next did her windscreen, staring into the face of a sleeping child, her son. He tried to see the woman through the smoke-smeared glass of the garage itself. She was standing by the phone. The boy was waking up.

Chapter Ten

While Frank made change in the office, she took the giant ring of keys that hung from the wall, then beat it like a tambourine, shouting, "*Olé!*" as she twirled.

Cal said, "None of that. Not in here."

Frank held out his hand, demanding the key ring.

"My, but this thing is heavy, why's it so heavy, Frank?" she said as she returned it. "Are you cryin'? Why's the bloody fool carrying on so, Cal?"

Frank pointed toward her car.

"Darn! Look at that. Just let me get my hands on him, would you!" she answered, while outside, front and back, the windows of the Cadillac shot up and down in a strange bad-tempered dance.

JOHN CASEY

Rapunzel

She is standing in the doorway of the barn loft, swaying backwards and forwards. Both her hands are over her head and flat against the inside of the lintel; her heels come off the floor on her forward motion, and she keeps her toes down on her backward motion, curling them around the rough ends of the floorboards.

She is looking over the low "L" of her house, across three fields of scrub, part of a salt pond, and a salt marsh, then the dunes at the back of the beach, and out to sea.

She is seventeen, and she is content because she's pretty sure she's going to be happy.

Her father is not as content as she is because he has a recurring notion that she won't ever be as happy as she is now. But he's happy about just about everything else.

Now she looks down at him, from the loft doorway. The light between them is rich, August light. The sun isn't directly in her eyes, but as her father is in the shadow of the house, and the smoke from his pipe hangs near him, and the light is so thick, she can't see his face sharply.

She makes a face at him, and she can see he's making a face back. She pantomimes running. She could say it out loud, they're only fifty feet apart. She mimes swimming with her arms and holds up one finger, meaning he must meet her in one hour. He looks at his watch, tamps down his pipe ash with the tip of his finger, pretends he's burned it, and puts it in his mouth.

He looks at his glass of beer, thinks he'd like another. He holds up one finger and a half, pointing at the half with his pipe stem. She shakes her head and holds up one finger. He gives a mock salute.

She holds her nose and puffs out of her cheeks as though she's about to jump out the doorway. He mouths the words, "But there's no water!," covers his eyes, peeks, pretends to follow an impossibly high arc out from the loft door, covers his ears when the arc ends, bobs his head watching the bounces.

This is not an everyday routine, but broken in enough so that he goes back to his pipe and beer without looking at her to see how she liked it. When he glances up again she is fitting the screen into the doorway. There are mosquitoes after sunset, and sometimes she spends the night in the loft. She takes the screen down during the day because it is such a fine mesh that it cuts down the light and the view. Now that she is standing behind the screen, fastening the four wing nuts that hold it in place, its bulges and planes catch the light so it glistens like an oil slick. She runs her hand over her side of it, checking for holes. He can see her clearly, and, having focused on that, he can now make out her face. It is beautiful. But in this light, filtered through the screen, it looks like a black-and-white photograph, and he is stabbed by the thought of her going away to college.

She seems to stay posed there for a long time. He figures out that she is having trouble with the last wing nut. Then she disappears, and he is foolishly afraid until he sees, through the ground-floor doorway, the bottom of the ladder move slightly and then her feet and legs. He thinks, She has another whole year of high school.

When she comes out of the house in her running clothes, she brings his bathing suit and leaves it in his lap. He says, "Don't nag. I'll be there."

There are still several hours of light left. It is a perfect day. He feels wonderful now, and there are still several pleasures ahead of him—he actually likes his swim in the ocean, and there are veal chops for supper, a Red Sox game on television. After, there is a new issue of *The National Fisherman* to browse through, and he's rereading *A Sportsman's Sketches*. He even has time now to put clean sheets on his bed before he walks to the beach. He knows he won't bother if he waits till after supper. He picks up his salt-stiff bathing suit and lumbers inside to get another beer.

Everett hasn't ever pinned down the reasons Vicky turned out so well, though he thought about it a lot ever since she was thirteen or fourteen. He thought for a while it was because she divided her time in equal thirds among solitude, friends her own age, and friends of his age. This theory finally came out too dry, but he stuck with this numerical method—the proportion of science to history to art; of schoolwork to sports to housework; of the eventful to the routine; of things she did that he was interested in to things she did that he wasn't. He knew it was silly.

His whole life he'd been apt to distract himself easily, and he thought that on the whole this was not a grievous fault. It also came quite naturally out of his work—he was a rare-book dealer. And a used-book dealer. He had a shop in Wakefield. In fact he had two shops—one a plain used-book store and across the street a smaller shop where he kept the older books and the first editions. The barn loft at home held duplicates, broken sets, and valueless but interesting odds and ends.

Everett did some work by mail as well. He'd had a lively trade in *Sailing Alone Around the World* by Joshua Slocum, before it was reprinted in modern paperback. Yacht clubs in New England still ordered his older mint editions to give as prizes.

On his own he was an aimless reader, but some of his friends kept him focused for at least short periods. Miss Lydia Perry, an occasional customer and probably his best friend, kept him up to the mark in natural history and New England literature.

Ruy Texeira, a fishing boat captain, came in looking for old books on weather forecasting and became another friend with a subject. Every time there was a storm that kept him in port, he'd turn up. A "foul-weather friend," Miss Perry called him. Captain Texeira eventually developed an additional interest in narratives of voyages of discovery. He was a man of more uneasiness than Everett himself could have lived with. Captain Texeira worried about the fishing business. He worried about the Catholic Church a good deal, too. On Monday, Wednesday, and Friday he thought the whole thing was nonsense that no grown man could believe, and on the other days he thought it was the only fragment of beauty and grace left from a better world.

Everett would argue with him a little, but the thing that fascinated him was that for all Captain Texeira's bemoaning the decline of everything, he was a tonic for Everett. And a tonic for Miss Perry, too. He gave Miss Perry compliments that Ev agreed with but wouldn't have voiced to her.

"Miss Perry, you have a noble mind."

And to Everett he said repeatedly, "What a lucky break I met you."

Direct statements of this kind, Everett and Miss Perry agreed were lacking from the conversation of most Yankees, the Yankee reputation of directness having its foundation chiefly in direct expressions of ill will.

Miss Perry said, "I remember my grandmother saying, 'Praise to the face is open disgrace.' That attitude was part of the same system of manners in which it was considered rude to discuss food, even to praise it."

Miss Perry went on to give the most impassioned speech Everett ever heard her utter. "Or even to express *any* quick enthusiasm. I grew up in a world of understatement and undertone. My father and mother were both very beautiful, they lived in a world of beautiful things, with none of which I could *do* anything. I was an ugly little genie in a crystal bottle of Manners, stopped up with a long crystal plug. It was only when I was almost fifty that I got out and was able, in my own voice, to speak—even as haltingly as I now do—of the beauty of Nature, or to speak of my friendship with my friends."

So a lot of Everett's worries about Vicky being an only motherless child dissipated themselves into the widening circles of his interests and friendships.

Vicky enjoyed her evening beach runs more than her other roadwork. She did a slow mile along the hardtop to the East Matunuck State Beach, hung her towel on the ladder of the lifeguard tower, did a decent mile down the rocky point in Matunuck. She clambered over it, then a dreamy mile past Willowdell, her eyes half shut against the low western sun, just able to see the glaze of waves across the hard sand catch the light, and then fade as they soaked in. She waded through the slough that ran from the sea to Little Salt Pond—cold water if the tide was flooding, warm if it was ebbing. She jogged until her legs were dry and then reached out with full strides until her thighs tightened or a little point of pain flickered in her shoulder. A trot until she caught her breath, then back to the slough at full stride. On the way back her eyes were open to the plaques of light on the western walls of beach houses, the sudden blaze from their windows. Along the dry upper beach, every swirl and hollow was mottled light and dark. Along the water line every stone and shell cast a shadow to point her way. As each wave reared up near shore, its crest grew green from the lengthwise slant of sun, then broke and spilled all the way to her feet, a long froth of released light.

She ran another burst up to the rock point and climbed over the boulders and slabs of undermined seawall. Another jog, another burst, until she saw her father coming across the sand to the lifeguard tower. She ran in and out of the water, kicking splashes through the tongues of waves. She made him walk with her while she pranced slowly, almost in place, beside him.

He asked, "Are you racing this week?"

"Oh yes. I'm going for both of the twins. I beat one last week. I'm not sure which one."

The twins were on the Chariho High School girls' track team. Vicky, who ran for South Kingston High, beat them both the fall of her junior year over a three-mile course, and in the spring on the track in the mile. But during the summer "Run for Fun" series, one or the other beat her every week for the first seven races over a five-mile course. She said, "This last race is flat. I can do it."

At first Everett had been alarmed at her exertions, especially when at sixteen she'd become obsessed with the idea of winning a track scholarship to college to save him money. There had seemed some taint to him in accepting her enduring daily pain—not to mention shin splints and plantar fasciitis—and he finally told her this obsession upset him. But she claimed to enjoy it, and he finally believed her when he saw her win the girls' mile at a track meet. She passed one of the twins (he couldn't tell them apart, either) in the backstretch with great sweeping strides, and it lifted his heart to see her at once so fierce and measured, so visible to the world in her intense flesh, her brown bangs matted on her forehead, her face and thighs pink with suffused blood—and yet she seemed to soar, to be concentrated so far aloft that she was free from harm.

It gave him a sense of freedom; this running was something he had nothing to do with, and he could begin to say to himself that she was not his creation.

Vicky had a period of tedious chatter about aerobics, cardio-vascular fitness, interval training, lactic-acid tolerance. He found her about the house doing sit-ups, leg-lifts, touching her toes with her legs crossed at the knee, or flat on her back with legs flung up over her head, or twisted to one side with her arms and legs coiled in and out. He grew used to her pretzel postures, but he was amazed to find her out on the road one cold rainy day, miles from home.

It was around the time that he noticed that she'd grown a great deal—her bones were larger, her shoulders flat but wide, her forehead and nose no longer pretty and girlish but large and handsome. He noted, too, that her running had reduced her can to a hard flatness so that her shorts hung slack behind. She looked so strange to him so abruptly that he took to looking in the mirror at his own face, and the first time he did, that took him by surprise, too. He didn't look as old as he thought he might, and much sharper around the eyes. And then suddenly, in mid-look, his appearance was strange to him. The eyes in the mirror caught his and held them. They were his eyes. "No," he said, out loud. "She has my eyes." Then he laughed, ran his head over his brow, and was at home again in his own face.

One day in his shop Miss Perry remarked to him that Vicky, for all her tomboy lankiness, had an exquisite mouth.

"But no derrière," he said.

Miss Perry frowned. But she went on to say, "On the whole you're a very good father for her, Everett—preoccupied, absent-minded, and yet companionable. I think it will be all right."

Everett was reassured by this statement. He looked at Vicky's mouth and saw that Miss Perry was absolutely right.

When Vicky reflected about her father—as opposed to worrying about what he was doing—she was mostly pleased and only mildly puzzled. She knew that he had loved her mother, but that he didn't brood, at least not within Vicky's memory—Vicky had been an infant when her mother died. She didn't think of his death—he was older than most fathers, but he never seemed to change. She was pleased that they got along better than most kids and their parents, and supposed that was because they were like a grandfather and granddaughter. She was proud of him—he was a hit with her friends, and she liked his friends. She liked talking with him, and even liked the way he liked her standing up to him. When she said, "Daddy! Don't ask me another question! Don't be so damned Socratic! Just tell me the answer, for God's sakes!" he laughed.

She missed him those afternoons when he was off on trips to rummage through books in old houses. But he usually called in from wherever he was to say he'd be back by such-and-such a time from Westerly, or Watch Hill, or Woonsocket, or even New Haven or Boston. When she was nine, she thought he knew everything, and it made her furious. She had a particular rage at his knowing foreign languages. She got over it at twelve when she began to realize that her father really only knew a little of everything: schoolboy French, schoolboy Latin. (Miss Perry *really* knew Latin and French.) He also knew a smattering of Italian and German, and he could say "I love you" in Swedish, "Life is a dream" in Spanish, and "Give me a little kiss" in Russian. At thirteen she found the guidebook to Rhode Island where he'd picked up that Matunuck meant high place in Narragansett. When she was fourteen, he announced that he was learning Portuguese from Captain Texeira, and she laughed. He still bluffed a few words of Portuguese because he loved the slushy sound and because he was an old show-off who didn't mind being caught bluffing.

He was nice to her boyfriends. He encouraged her to go out. But since she was in training, she didn't much. She found she liked being alone, or with him. She couldn't bear the thought of his eating supper all by himself.

The only time that she'd felt badly about how she behaved towards him was when she was twelve and made out a Christmas list. She wanted, as a Christmas present, for him to give up drinking (she'd read a list of the ten telltale signs of a drinking problem, and she calculated that he had at least four). He didn't say anything. Number Two: She wanted him to give up smoking his pipe in bed (there'd been a series of fire-safety lectures in school assembly). She didn't get through the third item on her list about his buying himself a new suit (in the winter he wore old double-breasted suits with pleated pants that were a foot wide from crease to crease—the jackets had horsehair pads in the shoulders. One day in the shop he'd had to take his off to pull out a horsehair that was pricking him, and everyone could see his suspenders that had naked ladies on them).

He'd laughed at her embarrassment in the shop, but he brought it up now without laughing. The whole Christmas list made him mad and sad in a way she'd never felt him be. He said, "Of all the peculiar things for you to turn into. A nag. And how could you possibly have turned out a prig..."

She cried. He came into her room and apologized. He finally made her laugh, but they were both uneasy for what seemed a long time. And he didn't just forget it all. A week later he bought a little metal clip-on cap for his pipes so that the embers couldn't possibly fall out. He stopped drinking more than a glass of wine at supper, but she knew that he occasionally finished the bottle after she'd gone to bed. She didn't mention that she knew. Even thinking about it made her bite her lip, but she wasn't sure which of her feelings it was that upset her, or where exactly she'd gone wrong.

She found herself watching what she said, and she could tell that he *knew* she was. He apologized several more times, which made her feel all right while he was apologizing, but afterwards she felt even more confused and troubled about how much she'd been able to do to him.

The end of this uneasy period came partly through time and partly through the intervention of Miss Perry. Vicky overheard part of the conversation. Miss Perry had a precise diction and an unhurried rhythm that carried beautifully all the way to the stair landing.

"It is perfectly natural that Victoria"—Miss Perry didn't like nicknames and especially didn't like *Vicky*—"at her age should start to worry about you in this way. I wouldn't be at all surprised if she also took an interest in organized religion. At the age of thirteen I became passionately interested in Mr. Hoover's War Relief. I wanted us all to help. I, of course, couldn't see why everyone didn't agree with me—I mean why didn't they praise me for reaching agreement with *them*? You see, I *assumed* I was only catching up to my parents, who had always been completely right about everything important, even if wrong about the small details of life. I soon found myself alarmed that I was having an effect on them. But I couldn't stop. It reached a point where I was punished for simply asking my mother how much a particularly splendid gown of hers cost. My father forbade me to mention War Relief at the table. But by then I could upset them just by looking at my mother's jewels with what they took to be an appraiser's eye. Finally my father promised to make a contribution. He cleared his throat and asked if I thought the figure he proposed was enough. Of course I had no idea at all. I said yes, but I was completely overwhelmed. I felt miserable, and I must have acted miserable because my father was puzzled. I think he really thought he had settled the matter so that we could once again be as we had been. For him that meant my being quiet. For me it meant his being perfect. I tell you this not to talk about myself, but to suggest that you and Victoria, although unlikely to reach those extremes of blindness on one side and violent impossible wishing on the other, should do something to break what can become a hypnotic pattern."

Vicky heard her father make several noises and finally give a sigh. He started several sentences but gave them up. He then said, "What a peculiar and sad story." Vicky remembered that he often began to talk like Miss Perry when the two of them had long conversations. Vicky almost gave herself away by giggling. She put her hands on the banisters so the stairs wouldn't creak, and went back to her room.

Vicky was struck by the story and spent a good deal of time imagining Miss Perry's mother's splendid gowns, the father's study, servants (a detail from other Miss Perry stories). Vicky knew the house well. When she was eight she even played with some dolls Miss Perry had played with when she was a girl. Vicky could see herself as Miss Perry at age eight, but not as Miss Perry now.

It was not long after that—only a matter of a winter and a spring, though it seemed a deep interval of time, if not a wide one—that Vicky took up surfing and noticing boys' looks. At fifteen she'd discovered that the boys she knew and even liked were dull to talk to, and fairly dull to observe most of the time, but that there were instants when some of them were suddenly and briefly wonderful to see. She was scared of being seen to be watching, and she also couldn't predict when a familiar face or body would burst into beauty, so that her hours of sunlit beach life were like looking for shooting stars on August nights. Just when you stopped looking, you saw out of the corner of your eye that you'd missed one. What she saw out of the corner of her eye was the mystery that most fascinated her, but she couldn't and didn't want to turn towards it full face.

She was completely at ease with her father by the next summer—it was then that she nagged him about getting more exercise, and they laughed about it. And then one day she was prattling on about karate (which the gang at the beach talked about a lot). She was telling third-hand stories about black belts toughening their hands by driving them into pails of sand, then gravel, and finally stones. Her father said yes, that sounded like a terrific program. He said, "I'll do it, too. I'll start by driving my fist into a pail of heavy cream. After a week I'll whip it." He laughed.

She told him not to laugh so hard at his own jokes. She tried telling the joke herself at the beach. It got a polite laugh, and then one of the boys said, "Your *father* made that up." His tone seemed accusatory, but she was pleased that this boy could recognize her father in this way.

The next joke was on Captain Texeira.

Captain Texeira asked Everett whether he was pleased to have such a devout daughter. Everett looked puzzled. He said to Vicky, "Are you devout these days? Aside from going to church with Miss Perry?"

Vicky didn't know what to say.

Captain Texeira said, "I've only seen such marks of devotion in convent schools. Turn this way, Vicky."

Everett said, "What are you talking about?"

"There," Captain Texeira said, pointing at Vicky's knees. "The calluses—they only come from hours of prayer."

Everett laughed. He said, "Oh, yes. Hours of devotion."

Vicky was embarrassed and cross to have these otherwise almost wonderful men rolling their round faces to look at her knees. "They're from my surfboard," she said. "I kneel on it to paddle out."

Everett laughed. He said to Captain Texeira, "You were worried, weren't you? You were afraid Protestants were horning in on your stuff?"

Captain Texeira laughed.

"Saint Victoria in ecstasy," Everett said.

Vicky narrowed her eyes.

"Victoria," Captain Texeira said, "the joke is on me. I was too free to say something. We are laughing at me."

"Quite right," her father said.

At first Vicky was annoyed at both men. But then she suddenly had a feeling of distance from them and felt tender towards them both. After thinking about it awhile, she supposed she felt that way because their feelings for each other had no future. Whereas when she fell in love she would be changed enormously.

The summer that Vicky was seventeen, which was nearing its end when she was standing in the barn-loft doorway, was the last period of slow time for them. Vicky's senior year in high school slipped by. She was bored by her regular classes but did extra work in her two advanced-placement seminars. She was captain of the girls' track team. She was conscientious in her captaincy, but wasn't disappointed when she didn't repeat all the triumphs of her junior year.

During the fall of her senior year, she pretty much decided she wanted to go to Pembroke, the women's part of Brown. One Indian Summer day she was in the barn loft reading. The screen wasn't up, and the sun shone in on her. There were wasps hovering under the eaves, but they seemed willing to stay outside. Over the near fields she could see puffs of milkweed seeds lifting in the slow air. Over the yard a strand of spider web floated across the light and disappeared. She leaned over to look at the porch. Her father wasn't there. She got up to go to the house to talk to him about college, but as she rose she felt an alarm at life now being in motion. She remembered standing in the barn-loft doorway the summer before without a thought in her head but with a feeling of the unmoving wholeness of the world, the forces that produced her life without her understanding them, without her needing to.

Her conversation with her father didn't go the way that she thought it would. He thought she ought to consider some other college than Brown. "How about someplace outside of Rhode Island? Or someplace completely different. Why not the West Coast?"

She said, "But you *love* Brown. What are you talking about?"

He said he didn't know. Maybe he felt restless and was taking it out on her. She said one of the good points about Brown was that she could come home weekends. She tried joking—she said he was just trying to get out of his promise to buy her a car. "If you don't get me a car, I'll come home weekends on a motorcycle."

He said, "Maybe it's just that I want to see some other places myself. I've been thinking how salty and foggy this place is. I dream of lemon groves. *'Kennst du das Land wo die Zitronen blumen?'* Or is it *Limonen?*"

"You don't speak German, Dad."

They walked down to the beach. It was high tide, as flat calm as at dawn on a summer's day, higher than usual, a moon tide in autumn. The surface of the water stretched out in bands of paler and paler blues, the farthest out so pale they seemed to be rising mist.

But even here, she thought again of herself in the barn-loft door. "Why should I ever leave here?" she said.

He said, "Adventure. Love. To seek your fortune. See the world."

"How is Miss Perry?" she asked.

"Up and around. She'll be okay."

Vicky thought that, though her father was peculiar, nothing much could change around here, and she could always have it—every shade of blue, every slash of light, and every shadow. She was now just eighteen; her father was sixty. She had no idea that their days could become different, that time could run at different speeds for two people whose days had begun and ended together for all her life, for all her life until now.

It would all go faster and faster. She would go to Brown. Everett would buy her a car, but she would come home less and less frequently as the terms went by. She would have a summer job after her first year and then spend a month at home. Later she would have summer jobs and take vacations with boyfriends, and she would spend ten days at home in August.

The summer after graduation she would take a "publishing procedures" course. She wouldn't find a job until she'd given up and was halfway through a year of graduate school. Then things would go well for a few years, not so well for a year, and then better and better. Better and better, but faster and faster.

During her job with *Oceanus,* a West German–financed magazine with beautiful pictures, she would spend fourteen months in Australia, about to return every month after the sixth, but always needed for another month.

She would be a good friend to several people, at least a necessary friend. She would also have several lovers over the years, but only one of them would become her friend, who would share her enthusiasms for what she did well and also her general sense of disappointment, which he knew he couldn't change but from which he could distract her. She couldn't imagine her father having passed through the life she was leading. She thought of questions about how her life had been, but when she went home for a quick holiday, he asked about her job, her prospects.

Everett would take some of the trips he dreamed of. He went with Captain Texeira for a month in Portugal. He would write Vicky one long letter from Portugal, adding a page or two each evening and only mailing it on the last day. Recipes, incidents, descriptions of Captain Texeira, Portuguese jokes he would claim to have translated himself, descriptions of three-hour-long suppers outdoors right in the middle of the village square from which the harbor was visible, and the sea. "One thing is very odd, the sun sets in the sea. Very disorientating for an old Yankee— why, everyone knows it's supposed to be the other way round. But I've got such good manners in my old age I don't mention it. And I could—I'm remarkably fluent now."

Everett died within a year of his trip to Portugal. Captain Texeira met Vicky at the Kingston Railroad station. On the ride down to Matunuck, Vicky told him she knew how much her father had loved going to Portugal with him.

Captain Texeira said, "Oh, we had a great time. We had the best time." He pulled over to the side of the road and burst into tears.

They drove on after a moment, but Captain Texeira stopped again before they got to Miss Perry's house. Vicky was a little scared by how angry he looked. His eyes were savage. She flinched from them. He put his palm over his face. When he took it away, his face sagged. But he began to speak rapidly.

"Anything," he said, "any help—to move things, pack up things. A car. I will be like a godfather, I have an energy left over from what your father and I planned to do. He had great pleasure in life. And his pleasure in life was double—Vicky—double. He traveled to Portugal. You traveled to Australia. He felt you there, he saw you there. Double."

Vicky felt herself withhold. She said, "But you, you did so much for him. He was so fortunate to be your friend." A version of Miss Perry's manner? A small correct likeness. No, that was unfair to Miss Perry. Miss Perry did not pour out (or hug or kiss), but she answered. She wasn't the extremes of Captain Texeira's open sea, but as discreetly as a tide marsh she absorbed and gave more completely than a stranger would know from the slow measure of exchange.

Vicky stayed with Miss Perry but didn't really talk to her at length. Miss Perry's voice was deliberate and clear as ever, and listening to her talk to others was a help. Vicky sat next to her at the service Miss Perry arranged. Vicky listened to Miss Perry's voice in formal prayer. When Vicky was about to leave, Miss Perry asked her to come back to see her, and Vicky was pleased to feel how much she wished to.

Vicky's friends in New York assured her that it was normal to feel numb and dissatisfied with the incompleteness of her feelings.

One night she woke up trembling. She saw clearly what she had just dreamed. She saw herself from below standing in the barn loft, her forehead and knees pushed against the screen; the air in front of the barn-loft door was thick. It was pleasant at first to see herself from the porch and to think of herself with affection. But the desire for her to come down through the air to the porch became terrifying. She could see the waves sliding onto the beach, she could feel the sun, she could smell the salt air, but all these passed quickly through the mind she seemed to be sharing with her father. Then her sight of herself began to fade. The sight of the house and the salt marsh filled her with terror. Vicky got out of bed, washed her face, and drank a glass of water. The feeling of terror was gone, but the sense of herself fading remained.

The next time Vicky had to go to Boston, she stopped off to see Miss Perry. Vicky told Miss Perry about this vision.

Miss Perry said, "There's little I can say. I don't think you'll have to have any of the kinds of difficulties I've had. I'm sure your father described them to you. I've been told they arise because I wanted to have had more affection, no, more *experience* of affection when I was a child. Everett's fear was that your affection for each other was too complete. But I do share this with you: In the middle of my life I thought childhood should have been the best part. And feared that perhaps it *had* been. That Wordsworth might have been right in some horrid way. My thoughts about eternity in my middle years were not altogether pleasant, although I maintained, when I was fortunate, the last hope of a Christian. It was only when I became friends with Captain Texeira and your father that I found a degree of happiness. It was not only that their friendship gave me pleasure, it was also that they encouraged me to take a bit more of a run at life. Captain Texeira is a very rollicking man. Your father was blithe. They both gave me to understand that what is sacred—although neither of them ever put it this way—what is sacred is neither fragile nor rare."

Vicky wondered if she loved Miss Perry. She certainly feared that Miss Perry would die, that when Miss Perry died, she would feel her father's death all over again, not just as an echo but as sharp as ever.

Miss Perry said, "Your father was not as fiercely buoyant as Captain Texeira, but he was buoyant, he was halfway between Captain Texeira and me in buoyancy. He understood us both."

Vicky looked into the shade of the tall trees. She thought of Captain Texeira explaining the cycle of water to her: clouds, rain, then water following the slope of the earth to the sea, running, seeping, but always moving to the sea, then swept in tides, currents, sinkings, and upwellings, until it was again lifted by the sun into the air.

She had asked him a question, she couldn't remember about what. He'd said, "That part comes tomorrow." She couldn't remember whether it had. What had always been a part of Captain Texeira's explanations—and her father's, too—was the sense that something was always going on somewhere else, but that it would turn up here sooner or later.

She said to Miss Perry, "The three of you seemed to me an unlikely threesome—I guess I thought that when I was in college. But it's not really so. What it is, I suppose—"

"Oh, don't *explain* it," Miss Perry said.

Vicky said, "No," but she thought what she'd set out to think. They all three circulated their friendship as though it were the water, though she couldn't say which of them was earth, sea, or sun.

This was just the sort of thought her father would have drawn out of her and turned into a joke, and without feeling any pang at all, she was glad he wouldn't.

She did feel a pang that she could think there were other beautiful places in the world, that the particular sights she loved first, she could look at now with knowledge, with knowledgeable comparisons. She wondered if it was horrible to let the view from the barn loft become just another view, or if it was fearful of her *not* to. She thought it didn't matter, it was happening to her. She rushed to think of its other seasons: snow touching the crisp grass in the fields and blowing off, covering more quickly the glaze of ice on the mud in the salt flats; a rainstorm so violent that nothing was visible but the absence of color—between frenzies of rain she could see the spray kick up white over the breakwater.

It was her father having these friends that made her think of what was *invisible* in her view from the barn-loft doorway—in the salt marsh the seepings under the thick layers of matted grass, their roots growing in season after season of their decayed ancestors. In the sea, the tides and coastwise currents, the water drawn up by the sun somewhere between Matunuck and Portugal.

"Captain Texeira and my father," Vicky said. "He did have a good time in Portugal."

Miss Perry said, "Oh, my dear! They had such good time! It would have ruined them if they'd been younger."

Vicky began to cry. Miss Perry touched her hand. After a while Vicky stopped crying, and sat quietly with Miss Perry.

Miss Perry got up and moved to the kitchen to make supper. Miss Perry was not a good cook, so Vicky hovered until she could politely take over the fish and vegetables.

At supper Miss Perry said she was thinking of taking a trip to Egypt. "Your father and I talked about doing it together," she said, "and of course I would rather have gone with him. But I think I shall go on my own. Do you know how we got a notion of Egypt? Your father once drew me a picture, a hieroglyph. He then said he would translate it."

Vicky laughed.

Miss Perry said, "He said it means 'Paradise is a man's own good nature.' I thought he'd made that up out of whole cloth, one of his bluffs all got up in Egyptian costume."

Vicky nodded.

Miss Perry said, "But it turned out to be quite authentic. The hieroglyph, and what he said it means. 'Paradise is a man's own good nature.'"

At first Vicky was disappointed. Then she was pleased.

"He had the *date* wrong," Miss Perry said. "I showed his drawing to a man at Brown. But otherwise your father had it right."

Vicky was relieved that her father's last joke had been to get one right. Then she was relieved because its authenticity, its being written in Egyptian, made her think how much else had disappeared before she knew about it. Someone ancient, too far off to mourn, had thought a thought that could have been her father's. Water appearing, disappearing, reappearing...Did Miss Perry mean her to think of that? It was an anesthetic, and she took it gladly.

Danger: Tulips

Hoping to find my way to the river, wide
with April's rain, and to see, perhaps,
a few wildflowers, and maybe a cardinal
whistling in a blossoming tree, I took a path
I'd never taken before, first through woods
and then a sloping meadow, across a fast stream,
then into another meadow, above whose green rise
appeared, with each step, first the slate roofs
and then the red brick walls of what I realized
was the abandoned state mental hospital.

My instinct was to turn away, but something drew me
toward those old buildings, each marked on the door
with a red X to show it was condemned.
The plywood filling the windows, painted red,
didn't keep me from imagining the scenes
that must have happened behind them,
the electroshock and the lobotomies.
So it was with relief that I saw the church
with its brick bell tower and mostly intact
stained glass, and made my way toward it.

I tried the door then noticed the red plaque
with *cancer* and *asbestos* engraved into it,
and backed away. Even the church
was contaminated. I wanted to get out of there,
to wash that place's toxins from my skin.
But circling around back, I found a garden
thick with weeds yet blooming nevertheless,
as it always had each spring,
with daffodils and purple hyacinths
and the reddest tulips I had ever seen.

Atlantis

About that country there's not much left to say.
Blue sun, far off, like a watery vein
in the cloud belt. The solid earth itself
unremarkable: familiar ruins
littered with standing stones our people
had lost the ability to decipher.
How deeply had we slept? Beneath the jellyfish
umbels of evergreens, each one a dream,
and the effervescent stars, strange currents
tugged at our thoughts like tapestries
unraveling into war. All spring
the nightingale perched on the cold volcano's lip.
The rats had abandoned the temples.
My mind was a voyage hungering to happen.

Beauty

is one of the greatest mysteries of nature.

*

Every day a pressure rises,
brutalities brew;

the pure in spirit are tried
as they accommodate

the mechanical demands
of the physical, repetitive world.

Repetition for Divinity is myth;
repetition for mortals is labor.

"Row, row,
row your boat."

*

The mock-Homeric and the beautiful
Alexandrian passages of Apollonius's Argonautica

Jonah in the belly
of the great fish

The avatars of prophecy and the institutionalization
of wisdom: oracle, sibyl, sage, book

The horses over
the doors of San Marco

The idea of a physical,
noble Greek antiquity

The French Revolution
cutting off the head of a king

The Mechanical Revolution
Skyscrapers

Assembly Lines
The Panopticon

*

With "imitation" one does not mean
slavish copying.... "What is imitated,
if handled with reason,
may assume another nature,
as it were, and becomes one's own."

Johann Winckelmann, a genius
who offered a paradigm:
that "noble simplicity
and quiet grandeur" might once
have changed the way

we viewed and organized
ourselves and others in the world.
Not a small order: moving realms,
giving the ideological
wheel of the world a little turn!

Backwards. Forwards.
Poor Winckelmann. So able.
So civilized. Dogged by loneliness.
Stabbed by a hotel acquaintance
and dying in Trieste at 51.

Near the Great Arch

There, in the same
spot as the annihilation
of the world, love
of existence stood. We
walked along. In boulevard
windows: plates, hat-like napkins
set for the imaginary
meal. Each act of
revenge has love as
a twin but could
art convey this without
violence? In this parabola,
I recalled the little
dragon in the painting,
that high, curly arch
of its tail like
a syntax being inaugurated.
Polka dots on emerald wings.
The knight stabbed it.
Maybe the vertical princess
prayed for it to live.
This was the end
of time; dread had
not returned to listen.

JANE HIRSHFIELD

Critique of Pure Reason

"Like one man milking a billy goat
another holding a sieve beneath it,"
Kant wrote, quoting an unnamed ancient.
It takes a moment to notice the sieve doesn't matter.
In her nineties, a woman begins to sleepwalk.
One morning finding pudding and a washed pot,
another the opened drawers of her late husband's dresser.
After a while, anything becomes familiar,
though the Yiddish jokes of Auschwitz
stumbled and failed outside the barbed wire.
Perimeter is not meaning, but it changes meaning,
as wit increases distance and compassion erodes it.
Let reason flow like water around a stone, the stone remains.
A dog catching a tennis ball lobbed into darkness
holds her breath silent, to keep the descent in her ears.
The goat stands patient for two millennia,
watching without judgment from behind his strange eyes.

Jason the Real

If I was a real guy,
said my friend Jason,
and I got an e-mail like that,
what would you do?

Someone had told him he was a big sexy dreamboat
and he was trying to figure out
if he should buy a sports car and a condom

or take an Alka-Seltzer and go to bed
to recover from the agitation.

You remember what that was like, don't you?
to be excited by an unexpected pleasure
that is almost immediately turned into a problem?

My friend Jason, gentle guy
with the blood galloping around inside his head
like a wild pony,

changing his shirt thirteen times;
doing the victory dance of the eligible bachelor,
combing his hair and falling over furniture.

That girl had knocked him out of focus
with her sweet words
about finding him pretty

and now he was standing on the Continental Divide
i.e., whether to remain continent or not—
But he didn't like having to decide.

It is so human to turn a freedom into pain
and it is so sweet when life
comes to teach you suffering

by giving you a choice,
and you twist and turn
in the little flames of possibility.

—But that is how you build your castle.
That is how one earns a name
like Jason the Real.

MICHAEL HOFMANN

Idyll

The windows will reflect harder, blacker, than before,
and fresh cracks will appear in the yellow brick.

There is no milkman or paperboy, but presumably
the lurid pizza fliers and brassy offers of loans

will continue to drop through the letterbox.
The utilities will be turned off one by one,

as the standing orders keel over or lose their address,
though there was never that much cooking or bathing or

phoning went on here anyway—the fridge will stop its buzz,
the boiler its spontaneous combusting—till there is nothing

but a mustiness of gas. The dust will coil and thicken
ultimately to hawsers around pipes and wires;

ever more elaborate spiders' webs will sheet off the corners;
rust stains and mildew and rot will spread chromatically

below the holes in the roof, radiate from the radiators;
eventually mosses and small grasses and even admirable

wildflowers, hell, an elder or buddleia, push their heads
through the chinks between the boards; a useless volume of books—

who could ever read that many—will keep the moths entertained,
generations of industrious woodlice and silverfish

will leave their corpses on the clarty work-surfaces,
and a pigeon or two will hook its feet over the tarnished sink

and brood vacantly on its queenly pink toes.

JOHN HOLLANDER

A Draft of Light

We all had to wear hats against the unvarying sun,
    Of course; but what was more significant,
We'd had to bring with us—along with our freshly prepared
    Thoughts, wrapped up in the old way—bottled light
To quench any thirst for knowledge that walking through the dry
    Valley of grayish terebinths and still
Lizards on chunks of fallen Hellenistic masonry
    Might intensify through the lengthening
Afternoon. Bottled? Well, all the available light, there
    In that valley uninflected by much
Shade, was barely fit to drink and having to bring our own
    Along was always part of the bargain.
When the light is too fierce for shadows to blossom in it,
    Too dry for any specificity,
Too general for distinctness, too literal for truth,
    What else, after all, can a person do?
Given that to think one's private thoughts of light were
    Somehow thereby to drink some of the fluid
Light that is at once itself, and what of it is brought forth
    Again both by all that it makes visible,
And by what those who see and say have ever said of it,
    As a flower whose name one knows jumps out—
Not merely in its saturated blue but in its changed
    Look—from the chaos of these petaled things
And those surrounding it. But light keeps one thing in the dark:
    The matter of its very origins.

Though babble's tall outrageous tower fell, crumbling under
    The weight of its own presumption, Language
Had a different tale to tell of itself: that it once
    Contracted to an insignificant
Point which nonetheless contained all the Meaningfulness that
    There was to be, and then this being quite

Unbearable, exploded into all the languages,
Chunks flying apart in such different
Directions! And then there were only all the languages.
Likewise with Light before there were the host
Of private lights reflected by each brush, dot, or pixel
Of all the surfaces of the seen world,
The world as seen. An untold story, this, and for
The matters of mass and energy we call
Mind, quite immaterial, but not to the substance of
Our long walk. Quite the other way: our walk—
Yes . . . nearing, but not at, its end, pausing there, just before
Leaving the valley for the pine-forest
Between it and the sea, we stopped to drink what was surely
Ours by right—we'd carried it along
The whole long way—and long swallows of it now allowed us
Rightly to claim to know now where we were
Going, rightly, at last, to know where we'd been all along
And where it was that we had started from.

Back Then

1.
My sea-blue father

Left me
Heart-burst

Broke as a dune does
Not glass, no cracks

A surge of softness
Slid down my throat

To stifle, for good,
Unendingness.

2.
My own me was haunted by a shovel
That chased me through the trees.

It called Hurry home to Mummy
And her theater of the drunk

Or "I'll get there first!"

3.
Yes, the Mannings were peasants.
And I bet I'm one of them.

Ireland and its cliff-torn charts
Are engraved in my psyche.

Sick around the rich.
Hostile and obsequious.
Communist, Catholic, and over-excited.

The potato eaters in my background
Never got to emigrate, only to wait.

They've been erased.

Now I ask for the grace to rent and not to keep.
Unemployment, oceans, and a drink.

What's in my bag?

A spyglass, a passport, some tickets, and a book,
A sandwich and a map of

A village before the eviscerations
Of Marketplace began.

4.
What you learn from torture
Is your physical nature.
Many lives pass before your eyes.

A little ramp down to a river
Before the tides increase the water
On the feast of Our Lady of Carmel.

Two children's foreheads
Before the inhabitation of mind of being.
Yes, God, I baptized them.

5.
In the true idea
There is no dying
Because the world is imaginary.

If a flash of green
Foresees our sun as a star
At least you lived among colors.

Adapt to the night
And since the world has already ended
No need to fear your sleep.

6.
"Now then.
Say The Lord's Prayer.
Now then.
I'll leave on a light
And change your sheets
And wash your brush
In the morning.

Now then.
Nestle down.
Night is drawing nigh.
The mourning dove coos.
The hedge is bittersweet
And the violet still blue.

The fuchsia dances
On many legs.
In the bath there's a spider
And in the hall
Some dust.
I'll get a broom
And a hot water bag.

Now then.
Your bed is fresh.
Our Father Who Art in Heaven.
It's 7 p.m., Dublin, 1947.
Be patient.
Your time will come."
Love from Grandma Manning.

from *Souls of the Labadie Tract*

Oh I see—I have to see
you fresh as those rough
streams are as power is

Caught—and wide awake

Oh—we are past saving
Aren't odd books full of us
What do you wake us for

———————————

Aren't we the very same
as we long ago saw and
little by little thought of it

Oh partly—not altogether

it isn't as if long ago—No
I mean the secret between
my age or any age—you

At My Father's Grave I Remember
T'ang Dynasty Calligraphies

Dispatched with a worn brush, the cursive writing
of poet Xaian Shu possessed heroic spirit.
His calligraphy's balanced characters
pointed to diligent study.

Scholar, poet, Mi Fu's idiosyncratic running characters
wrote of living in peaceful times before the Mongols
roared down from the north.

His writing was described as a "sailboat in a gust of wind"
or a "war horse charging into battle."

The long, slender strokes of Chu Suillang, T'ang master,
spoke of the donation of the body to birds and beasts.

Scholar-priest, my father signed his papers
in rounded letters slanted to the right,
suggesting an affable nature.

After the war, his bishop extolled in a letter,
"We delighted in his stories."
The dust of my father's body is donated to the mountains,
and wind brushes the name on his stone.

Familiar Rhymes

How naughty to run the car with a hose
    Returning the fumes
    To the man in the car
How lonely to sit in the fume-ridden car
    Alone on a Wednesday morning

How silly to end with your head in a bag
    A white plastic bag
    The end of your life
How awful to get the sack in the end
    All done on a Wednesday morning

How long can we waste our breaths in our griefs
    Pretending the world
    Has yet to know griefs
The car, hose, that Wednesday, the man in the bag
    Have outspent hours they're due of the morning

Cage

With my jade and pebbled hide, my fleas and magnificent
    talons,
Why have I long cooped under this iron bridge in Kittanning on
    the Allegheny?

See the green-bottle flies over the giant catfish rotting on
    a rock,
General Armstrong's hoofed men swarming down a hillside with
    smoke.

I want you to notice how thin my tongue is between my beak,
    and pink,
The same pink that edges the ovate clouds just after rush hour.

Look up. In spite of the roar of Exxon trucks, the whine of
    motorcycles,
The pigeons in the rafters line up in syntax with the nesting
    swallows.

The mother bats ricochet through coordinates of mosquitoes,
    gnats,
Bluish moths by the bank. I drag the day's net of mussels and
    books over the shoals

To my niche under the bridge. I suck in the cool slime of the
    bivalves,
I savor the ligaments that tie vowels to living bone. I sing for the
    butchered deities,

For the infants floating in the cattails, I curse the moon awake
    with words,
Hiss away the feral eyes. I release this flying cage into the
    darkened world.

JENNIFER L. KNOX

And Then There Is California

"There is science, logic, reason; there is thought verified by
experience. And then there is California."
—Edward Albee

The horizon gutted, skinned, unfurled
and dried like a diamondback, no secrets,
no secret sea cave stash, so evident it all seems
invisible: fissures in the orange San Andreas,
smoking asphalt on a runaway go-cart, 100%
clear skies in Funky Town, Manson said,
"There's no slack in my act." Mercury spread
so see-through thin, see this on the other side:

a girl dribbling gas into a fresh-empty 40
out on 10th and Ave. K: for the broke-down
Maverick or her friends to huff? Soon barefoot
before the swift, black aqueduct, nearly naked,
the parrot motif adorning her panties aquafies
her little butt peacockishly, but way cooler,
more Mexican—sudden color in a blinding
field of beige. The animals all live underground,
people shoot at nothing—water, the hills.

Pain Thinks of Something Biography

what it was without growing old a fever
a checkup the cold front dragging
a rake a plow Pain thinks of something

biography a place a word clearing &
threshing snow & leaves opening the hour
without growing old what it was Pain

thinks of something arthritis blindness
colloquy of field & figure light what
it was without blindness Pain thinks of

something biography what house & table
without growing old without *habitude*
without *offering* what evidence taking its meat

Possession

after Lena Cronqvist

Whose girls are these, Lena,
yours, mine, ours, everyone's?
So many deny them
(*Oh, no, not more of those!*)
Often your sister
Sometimes another girl
Always your parents
(For me dark is normal)

Is it conceivable
your parents or my own
actually could have done
anything deserving
of how the girls treat them?

In a glass bubble—
one to each figure-
head—more balloon than
retort, old Mom or Dad
twist and turn, wave stumps of
arms, press the glass with their
hands, shouting or shrieking—
air supply gone
              The girls
look delighted   Whose-
ever they are

Ours, our sisters, blond
or not, with or without
braids or bows, younger or

older   They play   They learn
cruelty   They—this is
hard to see—are learning
love

JEFFREY LEVINE

Blue, and Calling

The blinds of midnight are your hands saved from freezing.
Such is the heart, and that pause, the somber hollow beneath.
Sweet prophet, I name you and your ancestors fidget.
I say your temples spill with losses
and your shadow bursts with laughing.
I say morning thickens with peregrines, flowing soft
above the waves, flowing soft with tropic history clinging
to their talons, and the skies are flayed and silent.

Silent, as when the baker slips his first bread from the oven
and beyond, street lamps wick in and out, lost in mist.
Your lover pulls a blanket to her shoulders, returns
to sleep, while a thousand years in each direction farmers
mindless of cold bring in the hay, their chickens dusted with snow.

Winter sky whitens the roofs and shutters, the shrubs
and picket fences cloaked with morning light
and pitch-black birds perch across the inert country.
Here, your bed is a leftover, day-old, frozen,
hard as amber, clear as amber.

I live in your image as you live in mine, says the scripture.
That is why I send you a peregrine, blue, and calling.
A bird, a pond, night into morning, this small house
goes on living, your name in the fire, cured cordwood,
the air tastes every arpeggio, note by note.

GAIL MAZUR

Late September

after Vittorio Sereni

Now, from the sweet fragrance of roses
bitterness stings our nostrils. Our bay's
withdrawn from us, our beach littered
with broken things—splintered oars, bits
of old clay pipe from a long-ago shipwreck,
fragments of china plates. Exciting, those days
my townspeople scavenged rare cargo,
furnishing their long winters with random wares.

Now, the wind from two directions turns
soft dubious summer to a hard estate. Now,
when we know death is near, we can walk
with more courage, but slowly, alongside
cavorting dogs. And soon, he and I will wade
together into the cold homecoming wave.

Recognitions

Stories come to us like new senses

a wave and an ash tree were sisters
they had been separated since they were children
but they went on believing in each other
though each was sure that the other must be lost
they cherished traits of themselves that they thought of
as family resemblances features they held in common
the sheen of the wave fluttered in remembrance
of the undersides of the leaves of the ash tree
in summer air and the limbs of the ash tree
recalled the wave as the breeze lifted it
and they wrote to each other every day
without knowing where to send the letters
some of which have come to light only now
revealing in their old but familiar language
a view of the world we could not have guessed at

but that we always wanted to believe

Maddox Road

Shucking corn on the veranda, my sister said
she didn't care that her father had dropped by, or
that I'd finally met him. Later, after the dark

started to rake in, I found her outside again,
staring at the sweep of fallow fields and shadows
around our mother's rented house, the curious row

of weathered tobacco shacks along one edge, saddled
with their years of emptiness and disuse, and she said
this had all been plantation land, that her father's family

had worked here. He'd told her so, once, coming down
this road, and she had a feeling if she stayed here
long enough, something of meaning, of consolation,

might make itself clear. And because we're not close,
I asked if I could sit with her and we listened
to the pickups shudder past, invisible after nightfall,

and between them the diligent hoo of an owl,
listening for the rustle of what it trusted must lie near,
though obscured and impossible to predict.

Gradually, a wind bore the clumps of corn silk
we'd neglected into the unseen, its thickening
woods that press upon the darkened field.

ED OCHESTER

Pasta

In college I loved Browning's phrase—
was it in "Two in the Campagna"?—
"tangled ropes of lasagna" and even today
I think it may have been pasta which
civilized the Italians so much they
refused to fight for Mussolini—remember how
Marshall Badoglio's armies surrendered in Africa
tutti and *rapidamente?*—and even the names
make you smile: orecchiette ("little lambs' ears")
and orzo and penne and rigatoni and
of course gay bow-tie farfalle which
make me think of my favorite restaurant,
Flavio's, where the fat cook pounds his evil veal
but Nuncia is still beautiful and smiles as
she serves prawns and homemade fettuccine,
yes, and even surly Mencken called Puccini's music
"silver macaroni, exquisitely tangled"
and how lovely is "angel hair,"
semolina spun into a mist of pasta
that needs only some oil of the olive
and a few peppers or spring peas
to transport you to heaven and
whose preparation teaches
a great truth about cooking
and pleasure: focus, don't overdo it:
al dente, al dente.

Recycled

"This Book of Poems Has Been Printed on Recycled Paper"

Isn't it a form of reincarnation—
the sports page or an ad for vitamins
becoming, miraculously, the space
where a love poem finds itself?

a discarded shopping list
(cereal, oranges, soap)
returning to life as the backdrop
for a sonnet or villanelle?

I stare at each recycled page
and think about pentimento:
could lines from a diary
or a discarded prayer book

work their way through
these measured stanzas, lending
mysterious rhythms and weight
to another generation of words?

As when we put a loved body
in the ground, expecting finality,
and the newly nourished grass
exuberantly grows over it.

Summer, Florida Keys

Count on the storm to steel the waves,
tin their shimmer and heave. The electric
cracks sheen the air, particle its vapors,
and the wind that's coming has already
moved the sea, miles off. Shoreside,
we sense the sea has breathed in and readies.
Now, oiled by the hovering cobalt,
it simply rolls within itself like grain
in a sack a pair of fists is about to take
from dock to hold. Will throw the sack
on his shoulder, sweat will varnish his back,
and muscles will shift his flesh while the grain
finds its hourglass rules in the burlap dark.
We know the world's been held aloft
in punishment, and drowned in punishment.
But who carries it and why, to make of waves
a granary, of turquoise mirror a shroud?

Safekeeping

I stood on Mr. Silvia's porch with my last thirty-six dollars rolled in a rubber band tucked between breast and belly fat. I remembered the house from when I was a kid. Back then it was a gap-toothed barn where we played while birds flew in and out above us. Now it was a fancy house where the famous author, Bernard Silvia, lived. As I listened for him on the other side of the wooden door, I pulled my coat tight to protect against his eyes seeing me for the first time.

People noticed. They did. The polite ones tried to hide it, but everybody, meeting me for the first time, noticed. To get past the awkward moment, or maybe to prove her innocence, my mother always introduced me by saying, "Irene's heavy, but we love her," the same way she told creditors, "We're not Rockefellers, but we're good people."

It was useful, my fat, my flesh, for money or car keys or a handkerchief. It was the perfect place to soften sticks of butter for baking or to warm mittens. When I was little, before there were breasts, I kept things in the fat folds around my belly: a melting peppermint, a pink stone from the schoolyard, a pearly button. At bath time, my mother was disgusted by my hidden treasures. She set her mouth and quickly scooped them out of my flesh, then scrubbed the place hard with the soapy washcloth.

When my Anyi, my Hungarian grandmother, bathed me, she didn't bother with washcloth or soap. "*Kish csipash*, little stinker," she'd say, eyeing my belly folds. "What do you have in there?" And when I didn't answer, she'd say, "Good girl. Keep your secrets." With Anyi in charge, I soaked weightless in warm water, my treasures safe, and listened to her stories of ogres and flying wolves.

He opened the door.

"Come in, Irene," he said. And there it was, the moment when he took in all of me. He smiled with his celebrity-white teeth and held the door wide. I knew that when I walked past him he would allow himself to stare. "Go ahead and look," I wanted to say. "I weigh 337 pounds without my clothes on." But I was not my mother. I resisted the urge.

The barn house was big and airy inside, with stairs going up and a baby-grand piano in the middle. We sat on facing couches that each cost more than my car. He showed me a pad of yellow paper filled with his writing. There were words on top of words and arrows pointing to parts scribbled in the margins. Everything was printed in capital letters, though, and I found it easy enough to follow.

"Do you think you could transcribe this into the computer?" he said.

I was confused. "Mrs. Mack at job services said this was a housekeeping job," I said. I had been hoping for a nanny job, but this was all she had.

"It is," he said, "but I'd like it if you could also be sort of an assistant to me. I'll pay more, of course."

I couldn't believe my luck. I got good grades in school. I liked to read. A job that used those skills would be a marvelous thing in a world where only skinny, college-educated girls got those kinds of jobs.

So I became his assistant in the mornings, his housekeeper in the afternoons. I cooked the evening meal and slept in a room off the kitchen. Each morning I made strong black tea to tone down his over-white teeth. We worked upstairs, high in the treetops, our heads in the rafters of the barn house. The trees nodding outside the glass were bumpy with the coming spring, but still bleak and bare in the gray sky.

Bernard wrote at his desk on pads of yellow paper. He wore a gold ring with a ruby on his pinkie. I sat at the other table in front of the window. There, I untangled the scribbled words and entered them into the computer. We didn't speak. If I had a question, I would mark the page, and at the end of the morning's work we looked at it together.

On the third day he handed me two pages of scratchings that were an attempt to describe a street in the story. It must have been an important street, but the more he tried, word after word, sentence after sentence, to describe it, the more tangled it got.

"If you don't mind my saying so," I said, "you could just leave it out."

I waited for him to remind me I was only a housekeeper, but he read the page again and crossed out the entire passage.

That night, after laundry and sweeping the floors, I made chicken *paprikash,* Anyi's recipe, with the paprika so strong my eyes burned. Bernard ate two full plates and wiped them clean with bread. He smiled and poured wine for me. "It's good," he said.

At the end of my first week, a couple of owls no bigger than my shoes began poking in and out of a hole in the tall birch outside the workroom window. They were white with rusty streaks and round yellow eyes. They brought dry grass and twigs and dropped them into the cavity.

Early in the morning and at dusk especially, the two owls swooped in and out of the tree. I watched them, day after day, building for their babies, and I knew that Bernard watched them, too, because I could feel him look past me, out the window to the birch tree.

"Look at them fuss," he said, one day when the female hovered, pecking and hooting at her mate while he tried to place the grass he carried in his beak. "Poor bastard, he can't do anything right."

"Well, she's the one with the eggs," I said. "She has to have the perfect soft place to lay them."

The next morning the female was inside the tree; her round eyes shone in the gloom. Her mate continued his business of flying to and fro. She sat with her fierce eyes focused on me as if to say, "See the trouble I'm in? Now I have to lay these eggs, and he's free to fly."

After our morning work I dusted the barn room and piano, cleaned Bernard's bathroom, and then began preparing a special dinner. It was a celebration, after all; the mother owl had begun to lay her eggs. I ground pork and beef and made paprika roux for the stuffed cabbage rolls Anyi called *toltot kapusta.* I started the dough for dessert pancakes, *palacsinta,* and left it to rise under a tea towel, then I set to work grinding poppy seeds for the sweet filling. It was a laborious meal, one that Anyi made for large groups of family on special occasions. Tonight it was just for Bernard and me.

At six o'clock he came into the kitchen. I was rolling the meaty sauce into steamed cabbage leaves and arranging them in a baking pan. He took his ruby ring off and set it on the windowsill above the sink before he began to wash his hands.

I said, "Dinner will be ready in an hour."

He smiled his apologetic smile. No doubt about it, the teeth were a much better color since he had been drinking my tea.

"I thought I told you I'm going out," he said.

I kept filling cabbage rolls. He went off in his car. Of course, it was his right to go. He didn't have to tell me his plans.

After the cabbage rolls were in the oven and the pancakes were cooked and filled, I cleaned the kitchen. I did the stovetop and the floor. The pancakes were stored in a clean refrigerator. We would have them cold tomorrow. I ate a few, just to sample them, and then washed my hands in the sink. As I rubbed the soap between my hands, I stared at Bernard's ring on the windowsill. How easy it would be for that ring to go down the drain. I reached for the hand towel, still damp from Bernard using it. Either of us could knock that ring in the sink and never know we'd done it.

I scooped the ring up and tucked it in the crease under my left breast. For safekeeping.

Sometime between 12:30 and 1:00 Bernard came home. He turned on lights, opened the fridge door. I thought about getting up and fixing him a plate, but stayed put. Let him fix his own snack. Let him know what a good hot dinner he missed.

He stayed home the rest of the week and ate my cooking. We were making progress on the novel, though the characters, two lawyers, didn't seem to be doing anything. I worked on, reminding myself that Bernard must have something in mind.

The female owl stayed in the hole through March and into April. At dusk sometimes, I saw the male owl bring her mice. Once I saw him bring a small frog. Sleety rain blew in her face, and she squeezed her eyes shut. When the branches thrashed in high winds, she stayed cozy in her tree hole, sleeping or watching me. I stared back, wondering what was going on in the dark beneath her. The presence of Bernard's ring in my breast crease brought a calm, serene sense of expectation. He never mentioned missing it.

On the first sunny morning, when tiny leaves were showing gold-green in the tree, the female owl was gone.

"Look at that," Bernard said, resting his hand on my shoulder as he looked out the window. The warmth of his hand sank through my skin and wrapped around my bones.

"She's gone," I said.

"She'll be back."

I couldn't concentrate on typing Bernard's words into the computer for fear about the mother owl. It was not right that she would leave after so many days of sitting on the eggs. If the babies had hatched, she would be bringing them food.

"They haven't hatched yet," I said.

He said, "Nature has its own way, Irene."

After a wretched morning she still hadn't returned to the nest. I ate lunch and then went outside. I walked around the base of the birch looking for signs of her, circling ever wider, searching under bushes and on the ground. When I reached the porch of the house, I knew that I had found the spot. There was a worn place in the dirt where an animal had dug an entrance.

At my size, kneeling on the ground is a huge undertaking, but I did it, and I'm sorry to say that in the dark damp under the boards I found what I was looking for. White and brown feathers were everywhere, and in the midst of it there was the gutted carcass of the mother owl. Next to it sat the black cat that ate her.

"*Zoldog matcska*," I hissed at it, the way Anyi would have. Demon cat.

Rocks and small sticks pressed into the flesh on my knees. I scraped her feathers into a small pile and put them in the pockets of my sweater. A shadow crossed me, and I looked up to see Bernard.

"What did you find?" he said, extending both hands to help me rise.

I took his hands and waited for him to brace himself, leaning all his weight backward from our straight arms, to bring me to my feet. He managed the maneuver gracefully, as if he'd done it before.

"We have to save the eggs," I said, firmly, when I had caught my breath.

He shook his head. "Irene, don't interfere. We can't save them. We can't even hatch them."

But here he was wrong. I'd had in my mind, ever since I saw the mother owl sitting on her eggs, a woman from Anyi's stories. The woman had a magic goose that was sitting on a magic egg when a wolf ate her. The woman couldn't save the goose, but she took the egg and placed it between her own breasts. That egg between her breasts entranced me. There it stayed night and day, safe from the wolf. Eventually the magic gosling emerged and in gratitude granted the woman three wishes. I thought of this story, and I thought of all the things I had kept in my creases. Why not owl eggs?

"Bernard," I said. "Get the eggs. I can't climb a ladder, so you'll have to."

He must have seen in my eyes that I wouldn't back down, because he didn't argue. He brought the ladder from the shed and climbed up the side of the building until he could pick the eggs out of the tree.

"Be careful not to drop them," I shouted. He climbed down, holding the eggs in his shirt, mumbling under his breath, but he handed me four chalky-white eggs the size of apricots. I took them into the warm kitchen with Bernard following.

"I suppose we could get an incubator for them," he said.

He didn't know what I planned to do, and I wasn't sure how to explain it. I decided to indulge his whim about the store-bought incubator. It would be useful after the babies hatched. He searched in the yellow pages and made a phone call. Then he set off in his car to pick up the incubator.

I waited until he was down the hill and on the main road before I lifted my shirt and my right breast and placed some of the mother owl's feathers in the deep crevice. Then I put in two eggs, carefully insulated from each other with some of the softer down. I did the same on the other side. Now I had four eggs inside my creases. Plus the ruby ring.

The eggs themselves were cold at first, but within minutes they warmed to the temperature of my body. Gingerly, I began moving around the kitchen, testing how well the eggs would stay in place. I wiped the countertop and got milk out of the refrigerator. I reached up, carefully, to get a plate off of a high shelf. The creases stayed closed, the eggs stayed put. I bent at the waist, just slightly, to open the oven door as if to see a cake inside. The eggs were secure.

I began to prepare dinner. I washed green beans and snapped the ends off. I put a tenderloin in the oven. I had begun peeling the potatoes when Bernard's car sped to the top of the hill. He got out, carrying a box contraption with him.

He set it up on the kitchen counter. It was really nothing more than a cardboard box with a light bulb socket wired into the side, but he seemed excited when he plugged the thing in.

"Okay, give me the eggs," he said, holding out one hand while his other tinkered with the bulb.

I considered the ways to explain. He looked up from the box and stopped tinkering.

"Irene, where are the eggs?" he demanded.

I swallowed. "I have them."

He looked around as if he would find them on the kitchen counter.

"Where?"

This wasn't the time to be shy. He wasn't a stranger. I pointed to the area beneath my breasts, where they were warming nicely. "Right here."

He cleared his throat. He stood up and looked at me from his full height.

"What?"

I denied myself permission to turn away, but I did pull my sweater tighter around me. "I have them. My body will warm them to the perfect temperature. Just like the mother owl. Don't worry, your incubator will be good when they hatch out."

He squinted his eyes as if the light in the room was very bright at that moment.

"You've got them," he said, stupidly.

"Yes, Bernard. I've got them."

I could see another question bubbling up in him.

"There's plenty of room for them in the crease between my . . ."

He held up his hand for me to stop. "Never mind," he said, as though he couldn't bear the thought.

Apparently, I had insulted his sensibilities by incubating owl eggs in my flesh. I wondered if the thought of my belly and breast so disgusted him that he would fire me on the spot. I waited for him to send me away, but he turned and left the kitchen instead.

I roasted the meat and steamed the beans, boiled the potatoes, and served them with sour cream and the first chives from the garden. He ate in silence, not looking at me. I understood. It was a very personal thing we were sharing.

The next day he behaved as if there had never been owls in the tree outside the window. He acted as if he had never brought the ladder out from the shed and lifted the eggs down. The incubator stayed where it was, on the kitchen counter, and neither of us mentioned it.

He wrote with his pen, and I pecked at the computer, entering his story and taking the liberty of removing the occasional excessive word. Bernard wrote better in the three days that I carried the eggs than in the four weeks before. His characters began to live in the world he had made for them. It was going so well that Bernard said I should give the housework a break, and we extended the morning sessions into the afternoons.

He went out both nights, missing my good cooking. While he was out I roamed the house. The first night I stayed up till daylight, when his car came up the hill, then pretended I had slept in my room. The second night I reread his handwritten work of the day. "Irene," it said in the margin. "Check this." I carefully tore out "Irene" and put it with the eggs under the breast on the right. With my name in his handwriting, the ruby ring, and the four owl eggs in place, I finally lay down and slept. In the morning he pretended he'd slept at the house all night. It helped to know I had secrets, too.

We worked through the days, and as I sat at the computer the eggs seemed to pulse against my ribs, under my breasts, and I knew, the way mothers do, that the life they contained was coming soon.

On the third day, while transcribing a new draft of Bernard's fifth chapter, I felt the first sharp scratch on the underside of my right breast, and then I was aware of a certain dampness there.

"Oh," I said.

He raised his head.

"They're coming."

I looked out the window at the budding tree where the eggs had lived until they came to inhabit my creases. It came again, another weak scraping on my skin. I was aware of movement, of frenetic motion in the eggs.

Bernard stood up, every inch of him nervous and expectant. His eyes ran along the curves of my body. Never had a man looked at me like that before, curious about the mysteries my body contained. It made me blush, but I liked it. Yes, I did indeed. Suddenly, with life about to issue forth from my flesh, I was solid and beautiful. In that moment I saw myself as he must have been seeing me: perfect and whole.

"Is everything . . . are you all right?" he asked.

I walked to the stairs, and he was at my side, solicitous, his hand on my elbow. We went into the kitchen. Bernard hovered until I finally had to laugh, he was so nervous. "For goodness sake, Bernard, turn on your incubator," I said.

He plugged it in. I felt another sharper scratching under my left breast. I looked at Bernard. This was it.

I showed him how to cup his hands. "Like this, Bernard. Bring them close. Now don't drop it when I give it to you." He solemnly agreed.

With my left hand I lifted my right breast under my shirt and with my right hand scooped up the first egg and transferred it to Bernard's ready hands along with some of the owl feathers. I kept the paper with my name where it was.

Bernard's mouth opened when he held the little cracking egg. Our eyes met. He placed the egg carefully in the incubator.

I scooped up the second egg from under the right breast and gave it to him. This one wasn't as far along, but there was a hole in the eggshell where the tiny beak had broken through. Once it was safely in the incubator, we removed the two from under my left breast the same way. Warm from my heart, from my blood, they moved to Bernard's hands and into the incubator. His ruby ring stayed behind.

We abandoned work for the day, pulling stools up to the counter to watch the owls break out of their shells. At first, after moving them to the incubator, the hatching slowed so much that I worried they had stopped. I was beside myself. What if it wasn't warm enough in the box? Or worse, what if the bulb was too hot? How could any contraption compare to the steady dark warmth of my body?

Eventually two of the eggs started showing movement again. They pecked steadily at their shells from the inside, and I could hear them peeping, until finally the shells cracked open and there they were, a pile of right angles and damp fuzz, struggling to master their unrestricted bodies. They were caramel gold with huge round eyes and white triangles on their foreheads. Watching them, I realized I had been holding my breath. Bernard's eyes shone.

Before the first two owlets had fully dried in the light bulb heat, the other two began to peck again and soon freed themselves to join their siblings in a happy ruin of shells and feathers.

We laughed, Bernard and I, over the top of the incubator box, proud of the babies and ourselves. I excused myself and went to the bathroom. I placed the ring and the scrap of paper on the counter next to the sink. The warm washcloth felt good on the raw skin of my breast creases where the eggs had been, but I was already a little empty without them, a little sad they were gone. It was much better when I returned the ring and paper to clean, dry creases. When I went back out, Bernard was hanging up the phone.

"I called my friend to come see them," he said. "I hope that's okay."

I would have preferred to stay as we were, just we two alone with our owlets, but if Bernard had a friend who wanted to visit, of course I couldn't object.

He joked with me. "What do we feed owlets, anyway, chicken *paprikash*?"

"How about an earthworm?" I said.

I stayed with the owls while he went to the garden to dig for worms. I smoothed the gold fuzz on their little backs with my finger. They turned their round faces to me and opened their beaks.

"Soon, soon, my babies," I crooned. "Papa is bringing a nice fat worm."

The largest owl was pale cream with a dark spot on his ruff. I decided to call him Dirty Harry, after Anyi's favorite American movie. The smallest, palest owl I called Teeny. The other two were darker, the color of baked biscuits and honey, so the larger one became Biscuit and the smaller one Honey.

I heard Bernard's friend driving up the hill, but I stayed with the owlets, not wanting to leave them alone for a minute. I was sure the man would see Bernard out in the garden. In a moment the kitchen door opened, and I looked up, ready to welcome Bernard's friend. But it was a woman that came through the door in front of Bernard, wearing slim blue jeans and a black sweater. "You must be Irene," she said, holding out her hand. I kept my own in the incubator with the owlets. "This is Brenda," Bernard said to me, over her shoulder. "And here are two earthworms." He triumphantly held out a paper cup with the worms. He was slightly embarrassed and awkward as he slipped an arm around Brenda's waist.

I took the cup, what else could I do? I could see that Bernard thought of me as something completely other than this woman he brought into my kitchen and nuzzled in front of my face. The work of many days and the hatching of the owls were nothing compared to what he wanted with her. I had been stupid, stupid! to believe anything else.

Bernard leaned his head down so that it was resting on Brenda's shoulder, and he was watching me from there. The woman continued to give me the smile some people have for waiters and shopkeepers. It says: See how well bred I am, but please don't be mistaken; you are not my friend.

The owls began to peep harder, making a noise I couldn't ignore. I knew I must take care of them, so I busied myself with the earthworms. They were, indeed, two fine fat ones. I thought a moment about how the mother owl would have fed them to the owlets, then I got a kitchen knife and diced one of the worms on the cutting board. Brenda's hand went over her mouth at the sight. I scooped the chopped worm into another cup and then contemplated how to get the mash into the baby owl beaks. A spoon was too large and awkward, an eyedropper too fine and small. Finally, I fetched a plastic milk straw.

"Brilliant," Bernard said.

"Oh, my Lord," Brenda said, watching me suck the worm mash up into the straw. Of course I didn't pull it up far enough to touch my mouth, but I didn't bother to tell her that.

I placed my finger over the end of the straw, creating a vacuum so that none of the mash ran out. Then I positioned it over the open beak of Dirty Harry and released a small amount of earthworm. The surprised owlet closed his beak and swallowed, blinked once, looked up at me, and opened his beak again. I repeated the process. Now the other three made more noise, sensing that food was near, so I fed them.

The woman turned her head to better see Bernard. "So, how long were they in the incubator?"

Bernard didn't hesitate. "Three days, right, Irene?"

I didn't answer. Let him tell his own lies. I knew the truth: the skin under my breasts was raw from hatching those owls.

I fed the owlets in turn until the straw was empty. The second worm was prepared and devoured the same way. Still, the owlets peeped for more. I rinsed out the compost bucket and handed it to Bernard. Dusk was already thick outside. "More worms," I said. "Lots of them, before it gets dark. I've no idea how much they'll eat, so if you don't want to dig in the middle of the night, fill the bucket now."

They went out together. He said something under his breath. She stifled a laugh. When they were gone I sank onto one of the stools by the incubator, the pain in my heart pulling my head down to the countertop.

What could be done? How had I let this happen? The pain expanded to my ribs and shoulders. My breath came raggedly because of it.

Bernard and the woman came back into my kitchen, rosy-cheeked and holding on to each other. I accepted the bucket of worms and filled the blender.

"We got lucky," Bernard said. "There was a huge knot of them in the compost pile."

"You realize we must feed the owls through the night," I said severely, pushing the pulse button on the blender.

Brenda flinched at the sight of the worms becoming mash. "I'd like to help," she said, looking up into Bernard's face and asking other silent questions.

Bernard glanced at the gory blender and cutting board. "What about dinner?"

I began feeding the owlets with the straw. Let him clean up. Let him cook his own dinner.

"We could order Chinese," Brenda said.

Bernard looked at me. This would be the first time I didn't cook for him. "Do what you like," I said. "I'm not hungry."

"Irene, you're tired," Bernard said. "It's been a big day with the owls hatching. Why don't you go rest and let us take the first shift?"

I continued to feed the babies. Dirty Harry was the best eater. Surprisingly, Teeny was the second best.

"You? You don't know how to feed them."

Brenda answered. "We've been watching you. We see how to do it."

"You're going to suck worms into the straw?"

Bernard quickly said, "I'll do that part."

I was suddenly exhausted. My chest hurt, my hand was heavy, and my eyelids drooped as I fed the owls.

"Okay," I said. "Let me see you do it."

They exchanged a look that told me they had agreed to humor me.

I went on. I was a dumb beast putting my head down and plodding forward. "You have to get Biscuit and Honey to eat. They're slower than the other two."

Again, they traded a glance.

"You named them?" Brenda asked.

I pointed out the differences between the owls and taught them the names. I watched Bernard feed them. Then I watched Brenda feed them. I made sure they knew not to put too much mash in at once. When I was satisfied that the owls would be all right, and I had Bernard's promise to wake me in two hours, I went into my room and lay on the bed, still in my clothes.

It was late, much more than two hours later, when Bernard knocked on my door. I came out to a kitchen full of cartons from Chinese food along with dirty plates and an empty bottle of wine. The blender sat where I'd left it, and now the worm mash was black and hard on the inside. Brenda was sleeping under a blanket on the couch. Only a faint peeping came from the incubator.

"I'm beat, Irene. I've got to get some sleep," Bernard said. "Two of the owls haven't eaten in a while, I think they finally got full. The other two are still hungry all the time."

I looked into the box. There was spilled worm mash dried everywhere, on the mother owl's feathers, on the sides of the box. Dirty Harry and Teeny were stronger and making little hops in the mess. Biscuit and Honey were over in one corner, huddled together. I could see that they were not good.

I picked up Biscuit and held him in my hand. I tried to feed him. He didn't open his beak. I stroked his back and then his front with my finger to try to get him going. He just looked up at me with a fearful eye. I could feel his little heart hammering in his chest. I brought him to my mouth and blew gently on his face to try to get him to open his beak, but he just closed his eyes.

I turned on Bernard. "How could you let this happen? Why didn't you wake me?"

He shook his head and opened his arms in the classic gesture of innocence. "They stopped eating. I thought they were full. Anyway, there isn't anything you could have done."

I put Biscuit down and picked up Honey. Her heart was erratic. Her eye was already looking far past me. I knew she would die soon. I held her to my heart and felt myself begin to sway.

Bernard put his hand on my shoulder, and I'm ashamed to say that even at that moment, when I had already lost him and I knew I was about to begin losing the babies, I was grateful, grateful! for his touch. "I'm sorry, Irene," he said. I gritted my teeth, waiting for him to add how it wasn't his fault. I was almost hoping he would, so that I could hate him completely. But he didn't. He moved away from me with the air of a man who accepts the burden of blame, fairly placed or not. He woke up his girlfriend and helped her to his bedroom. The door shut.

Still holding Honey, I scooped up Biscuit so that they were both together. I sang a Hungarian lullaby to them. I tried to forget about Bernard and the woman behind the closed door. I kept singing as first one and then the other owl's little sides stopped heaving and the eyes grew dull. I sang as I lifted my left breast with my right hand and put Biscuit and Honey back in the fold with Bernard's ring. I wanted to keep them safe and warm while I took care of Dirty Harry and Teeny.

At dawn I knocked on the door to Bernard's bedroom. He opened it, wearing only boxer shorts. I averted my eyes and held out the compost bucket.

"Excuse me, but we need more worms."

He stepped into his pants from the night before. I caught a glimpse of the thin, bare arm of the woman in the bed. He grabbed the bucket and went outside.

I began to clean the kitchen. I collected dirty glasses and plates, threw away Chinese food cartons, put hot sudsy water in the blender, and turned it on to clean the dried worm mash out of the blade. All the time I was aware of the two dead owlets and his ruby ring tucked into the crease under my heart. I worried about the two remaining owls. Was Teeny eating less than she had been? Was she looking droopy around the ruff? I busied myself cleaning the spills of worm mash off of the incubator box. I folded the blanket that the woman had used and placed her shoes neatly by the door.

When Bernard came back with the worms, I whipped them up. He looked into the incubator. "What happened to the brown ones?" he asked. He didn't say their names.

"They died."

"Oh," he said, with less interest than if I had told him I had broken a teacup.

I said nothing more. My chest ached into my arms.

"Irene, you look awful. Go back to bed, and I'll feed these two for a while."

But I had learned at a terrible price what came of letting him care for them. I was not going to risk Dirty Harry and Teeny. I would feed them alone.

By noon the woman was up, and, tired of the owls, she went back to her own house. It was clear to me now that Teeny was not eating as much.

"Call a veterinarian," I said to Bernard. "Find out what can be done."

He called a vet and the county extension and the department of wildlife. They all said that the only thing we could do differently was try another food; that the owls should be getting small birds or mice.

I stroked Teeny. She was taking very little mash now.

"I'll drive to the pet store in town and get some mice," Bernard said. He looked haggard. I could see he wanted this to be over.

While he was gone, Teeny died. I placed her back in her birth-place, underneath my right breast, next to my name in his hand-writing. My body felt strangely light. The pain radiating from my chest was cleansing and pure. I hadn't eaten for over a day. I had slept only a few hours. I was the living repository of dead owls. I wandered through the house that I had cleaned many times over the last five weeks. I went up to the writing room and saw his pads of paper and the computer. I turned on the computer and gazed outside at the cavity in the tree where the owls had nested. I dragged all of the chapters I had typed into the picture of the trashcan on the screen and then emptied the trash. Yes, I told the computer, I was sure I wanted to empty the trash.

I put all of the scribbled yellow pads of paper and printed chapters into a garbage bag and dragged them outside to the compost where Bernard had dug for worms. My breath hurt in my chest, but I couldn't stop. I took the shovel and went to work, digging a shallow grave at the base of the compost pile. I was sweating and nearly faint from the effort and pain before it was deep enough. I emptied the bag into the hole and put compost and dirt back on top, amazed that I could do such work. When the dirt was in place, I walked around on it and then shoveled compost over it so that he would never know what was rotting at the bottom.

I was back inside with Dirty Harry, feeding him the last of the earthworms, when Bernard's car roared up the hill. He came through the door with mice in a box.

"Teeny's dead," I said, accepting the box. It moved like a large Mexican jumping bean. I dropped one white mouse into the blender and watched it run around on the blades a moment before I pushed the pulse button.

Bernard winced. "That was harsh."

I meant to shrug my shoulders, but knives of pain went through me. I meant to say, "You think that was harsh, Bernard? That mouse was lucky. He didn't feel a thing." But I no longer had the strength. I was going to pick up Dirty Harry and try some of the mouse puree on him, but I began to sink. My legs refused to keep me upright.

Bernard grabbed my elbow, then moved a chair to catch me as I went down. My full weight landed in it at once, and it gave out with a loud crack. I added this to all the other shame that was breaking its way out of my chest.

It took the ambulance a long time. Bernard put his arms around me to keep me from falling over.

"Please don't die," he whispered.

Somewhere between Bernard's house and the hospital, they put the shockers on my bare chest, and, with Bernard watching, my shame was immense. I began to rise. I floated above the pain and noise and the paramedics working.

When I woke up I was in a bed in a quiet room. On the table next to me, on a clean white towel, were the three dead owls, the ring, and the paper with my name.

Tears puddled into my hair and ears. I had been turned inside out like a pocket. My body had given up all of its secrets, and now I was empty. I was too weak to raise a hand and wipe my eyes, so I lay there and cried until the nurse came in and put something into the IV.

The next time I woke, Bernard was talking to the nurse. I kept my eyes closed. The lids were too heavy, and, anyway, I couldn't face him, after what he'd seen, after everything that had happened. He pulled the chair up to the bed and sat in it for a long time.

"Irene," he said. I didn't open my eyes. Let him talk to me as if I was asleep. Let him talk to me as if I were dying.

"Dirty Harry pulled through," he said, and I almost opened my eyes for that. I had to remind myself to keep them squeezed shut. "He's at an owl refuge."

And then his warm hand was opening mine and putting in the ring and the scrap of paper and closing my fist around them.

The nurse put Biscuit, Honey, and Teeny in the hospital freezer as they were starting to cause concern among the staff. She brought them to me on my last day, three frozen lumps of fluff and beak in a Ziploc bag.

There was no discussion about where I would go when I was able to leave the hospital. I was moved into my mother's house. My clothes and things were in two boxes. Bernard must have packed them.

I had one last task before I claimed my birthright. I took the owls into my old room, the stale-smelling, cramped bedroom where I had begun. I ripped my white cotton shirt into strips and wound each of the three birds, starting at the tiny feet and wrapping up over the head and back down again, several times, until each bird was a mango-sized mummy. I did the same with the ruby ring, and the paper that said "Irene." I tied the cotton ends into knots and packed them all into the small box, tucking the remaining shirt around them. I taped the box and printed his address on it. My mother took it to the post office. When she was gone I pulled back the covers and got into my childhood bed. Outside the window the branches were glutted with leaves. I listened to my heart beat its new, weak rhythm and imagined Bernard opening the box. He would mull over the contents before he emptied them onto his desk. Then he would pick up one bundle at a time and begin to unwind the cotton. I pulled the sheet up to my chin and began to wait.

The Dimensions of Silence

from House of Widows

Like most men under the right circumstances, my father could walk on water. In fact, he did it often, and sometimes he took me along. Together we stood on the frozen whitecaps of Cape Ann looking back at the lights of our town on the Massachusetts north shore. Even half a mile away they appeared as close and bright as tropical fruits, and I was tempted to reach out and pluck every one and deposit them in the sled on which my father had dragged me. Our load might have weighed us down, yet I knew Father could bear it. He was master of the waters, Neptune of the North Shore, slayer of cod, tuna, even shark.

Father would say: Look, there's Devon House and the Schooner Restaurant and the Gull Cafe. Though he didn't mention it, there was also the fish cannery where he went to work each morning at six. Standing beside him on the ice, I felt myself safer than anywhere since. We wouldn't talk much. I stared back, imagining Mother in the kitchen behind one of those windows making soda bread and mincemeat pie. While I gazed longingly landward, Father turned both ways: toward our house, and toward the sea. Had we glanced down, we might have noticed a web of cracks forming under our feet.

It was years before the fissures finally broke, setting us adrift in different directions, but the causes for the crackup must have been present even in that moment. They were the causes whose effects I've lived with ever since. Another name for it is *history*.

My father owned a boat, and sometimes he supplemented his income from the plant by doing a little wildcat fishing. Out at four, he'd return as darkness smoked from the water. Like most of his colleagues, he drank, though its effect on him at that time still seemed reliably soothing. But he was away a lot. At night Mother and I worked on projects together: we built a Viking ship out of peanut shells, painted what we thought the weather gods looked like, and made elaborate costumes for Halloween. Our preparations for it began in December. We hardly noticed Christmas. When I was seven or eight, I asked why, while other kids decorated trees, we were installing grow lights and planting pumpkin seeds, and my mother told me about Jesus. Mother's sister, my aunt Joan, was a nun, which made Mother an authority on the subject. She said Jesus taught you should love everything that lives, even people who don't like you. I said, I don't like Mr. Maynard, a neighbor who complained whenever we chased a ball into his yard. She said: You should try loving Mr. Maynard especially. Just try, she said.

As a boy, I stumbled amid mysteries. One morning I walked into the kitchen to find my parents at the table, arguing. The scene might have been captioned, in gothic letters, Anger. Father's head was thrown back. He breathed heavily through his stuffed-up nose. His eyes were shut. His arms, thick from hauling nets and hoisting crates, knotted over that chest he so often let me use for a trampoline.

Mother, always feisty, a chaos of red hair lashing her shoulders, leaned across the table with a letter, perhaps a bill, in her hand.

"We can't afford this," she said emphatically. "And Vera, too?"

Father tilted his head further back, as though dodging a blow.

Because my parents normally shielded me from their scenes, I panicked. Yet I was already aware of money, whose sullen magic engineered the appearance of everything from bicycles to summer vacations in the mountains. I suspect it also fueled the sharp words between them.

But in this case, money seemed secondary to some greater danger represented by the envelope in Mother's hand.

It took them a few seconds to acknowledge my quivering presence—their relationship was a kingdom unto itself, a place apart. One on one, they could be the best of company; together they often generated an exclusionary force field.

"Why aren't you in school, Tommy?" Mother asked.

"It's Saturday," I reminded her.

"Son," Father murmured without opening his eyes.

My great-aunt Vera's name was always a red flag for trouble. Vera and her sons were our last surviving relatives in Western

Europe. Or put it this way: she was the only figure from his past Father had carried over with him. She was the sponsor of all gratitude, the mirror's dark backing reflecting us to ourselves: *Finish your dinner, you don't know what hunger is. Have I ever told you about Vera?*

Only about a million times. A new version every year, each more gruesome than the last.

But until I was ten or eleven, he repeated the familiar yet always changing story about the winter Vera ran out of food.

Telling it, my father, that large, broad-shouldered man—his physical presence dominated my world, filling every room in the house—contracted, rattling the windows instead with his voice, which rose and fell like a winter wind howling over the bleak steppes to which we were suddenly airlifted.

She boiled her shoes, then served the broth to her three boys. They gnawed the leather, but it left them hungry. Finally, she swaddled her feet in cloth strips and walked out into the sub-zero snow-covered landscape to hunt for food. After days of wandering, she came upon a lone dove huddled in the crook of a poplar. The bird was out of reach, so she picked up a stone and hurled it, but she was tired and her arms were frozen and she missed. The second time, the bird wasn't as lucky.

She reached her house just as the stars appeared over the ice-covered steppes.

She slammed the door and rushed to the cold stove to check on her sons. There was one, and here another. But where was the third?

And then she saw what was left of the body, and the blood-smeared faces of the two boys staring up at her like startled animals.

She grabbed a knife off the floor and lifted it over her head above the eldest. He made no move to hide or protect himself.

Seeing his trusting gaze, she dropped the blade and threw her arms around both boys, pulling them to her. All three wailed to heaven for mercy.

That was one version. By the time he was done, sweat beaded Father's forehead and eyelids, and he rubbed his lips with the back of his hand, his eyes fixed on a point ten million light years away.

No one else I knew endured such mealtime tales.

"You expect me to eat after that?" I asked.

"Every last bit."

"How do you know this, anyway?"

"Vera told me," he answered, taking a long sip of Jameson's, watching me closely from under his lush brows. Even as a boy I felt there were holes in his story large as Siberia and one day I would drive right through them.

The problem, or the complication, is that my parents were by no means always at odds. There were times I'd catch them laughing over a game of checkers, at which Mother was ruthless, or they'd row out into the cove, abandoning me onshore—who knew what they did once they disappeared behind the rocks?

Many of our activities involved animals. We drove to Plum Island in late April to watch plovers building their nests and in August we went for the monarchs who stop there yearly on their way to Mexico. Once we found one with a broken wing and took it home. We created a terrarium from an old fish tank, pilfering my model railroad and building for the butterfly a miniature version of Devon, complete with Dogtown. Several times a day I dipped my middle finger in sugar water, then watched the insect tap the bead with its long feeding tube until it was more domesticated than a cat.

One evening, after finishing my homework, I'd taken the butterfly out when I heard the door slam, followed by Mother's loudest scream.

In the living room stood Father with something huge and black in his arms, looking like a mummy greased in glistening oil. It took a minute to figure out it was a baby seal. Winters, hurt and lost seals frequently washed up onshore.

"Fill the tub," he barked. "Cold water."

Mother did, but she accidentally turned on the hot tap, then went out of the room to grab some old towels from the laundry, and when she returned Father yelled at her, *"You trying to kill the pup?"* and she emptied it and refilled it with cold while I jumped about anxiously, excited by the new arrival.

The month before I'd done a report for school about the life cycle of the harbor seal. *Phoca vitulina concolor.* While their ancestors, fifteen million years back, walked on land, these were strictly aquatic, capable of remaining underwater for half an hour, able to plunge down three hundred feet. You see them lounging on rocks alongside their buds in the harbor, but basically they're loners who socialize mainly in order to mate and chill in safety.

Their courtship rituals, I told the class, included bubble-blowing and mouthing each other's necks.

Father deposited the creature gently into the tub, and it was then I noticed its flipper bent in the wrong direction. The three of us watched its black eyes staring out at us.

"Where's its mother?" Mother asked.

"Who knows," Father said. "Sometimes these little fellows get caught in a current and dragged away. If they can't find their way back before they're ready to be on their own, well, you can imagine," he said, wiping his face and hands on the towel.

Later, I returned to my room to find I'd forgotten to put the butterfly in the terrarium.

A window, slightly open, invited escape. I leaned my forehead on the glass and looked to the harbor. Lights flickered over the water, riding the waves to the edge of the world.

That may have been the first time I saw the law of exchange in action. The seal entered; the butterfly left. A trade had occurred. Unfortunately, I wanted both. Not being able to get both led in time to my theory of the turn.

It was nothing heavy, my idea that amid the world's variety you could find anything you imagined—indeed, your imagining brought the thing, life itself, into being; at any given moment the world contained everything you'd ever dreamed of—you only had to turn to it and it would come alive as though it had been waiting. Turning to one, you had of course to turn away from another. Everything gripped you because its very life depended on you. Without you, it would disappear into some other dimension.

I had turned away from Father, and look what happened.

Then there were those times when someone, or something, turned to you first.

The next morning Dr. Looby, the town vet, came by.

"You should bring it to the aquarium in Boston," he said after examining the seal and wrapping its flipper in adhesive. "It's a she, by the way."

"I should," Father shook his head, "but..." He looked over at me. "I won't. Tommy here could stand another companion. I'm going to be out a lot this winter."

"You know how much they eat," Dr. Looby said softly.

"Ten to eighteen pounds a day," I rattled off. "Shrimp, salmon, squid, and mollusks."

"That's going to be a tithe off your take," the doctor said.

Father shrugged.

That was how I wound up spending several weeks caretaking a seal. We bought a huge wading pool, which we set up on the porch in front of the house. I'd get right in with Sheba, who delighted in squirting me with water from her pursed lips. She put weight on fast. At feedings, she swallowed whole shrimp and clams.

I was beginning to dread returning her to the sea when, one morning, I awoke and padded out, still sleepy, eyes gummed shut, only to find her lying on the porch floor. She'd worked her way out of the tub. She wasn't moving. Her skin, normally glistening, had already dried and begun to crack. A fly circled her nostril.

I shouted loud enough to bring Mother running from the kitchen. We threw ourselves at the creature, poking and probing, hoping to revive it, but it was too late.

Later that night, Father had to carry her out. I wanted to bury her in our yard, but Father insisted the right thing was to send her home to the sea, so we placed her, swaddled in tarp, in the back seat of his Buick, and drove to the water. There, standing on the tip of the jetty, together we heaved Sheba back to the source. A bitter wind sprayed our faces. Father put his hand on my shoulder, and we returned to the apartment in silence.

Soon after, Father decided I needed to learn how to play the piano. Next thing I knew I was taking lessons from our downstairs neighbor. Once a week I descended to Ms. Johnson's apartment. The place smelled clean and inviting, as though she'd scrubbed the floors with cookie dough. Tall, big-haired, large-busted, and funny, she wore long, flowing, brightly colored dresses and earrings the size of basketball hoops. Romare Bearden prints hung on her walls, and an imposing African drum with a tight leather face rose in the corner of the living room.

Since we couldn't afford a piano, Father painted a keyboard for me on a two-by-four. I practiced an hour each evening, running my fingers up and down the keys. Mother looked at me skeptically, asking: "Can you really practice like that?"

I nodded.

While I had no ear for music, I possessed a lively imagination and could hear myself playing with no problem at all. The notes rose up in four dimensions. I raced through finger exercises, scales, and arpeggios. Before long, I preferred the notes I imagined to the sound of a real piano, which inevitably seemed a little off-key. I hammered away, window open, lace curtains swaying to my silent, pitch-perfect tune.

The piano helped, but as tensions between my parents escalated, school became my haven and my obsession. Mother posted my gold stars, certificates, and awards around the apartment. Visitors to the bathroom were invited to reflect on my "Reflections on *A Separate Peace*" tucked in between *Newsweek* and *People*. I quickly discovered how easy it was to please teachers, how little it took to get their attention and praise. I made sure my assignments were always longer and fuller than what had been asked for. A five-page paper on *Slaughterhouse Five*? Why not fifteen, or twenty, with footnotes? While my peers yanked at their leather mitts under lights that whooshed on as twilight descended, I huddled in the library. My interests included sailing, taxidermy, and Eastern European history. I studied photographs of stuffed dogs, cats, and lynxes, admiring their claws, bared teeth, and glass eyes opened forever—wishing I'd known of this option when Sheba died. Then I read about czars, and peasants, and revolutionaries—maniacs from Father's part of the world.

Maybe it was because of the seemingly disconnected stories hovering in the air, names without contexts, that, by the time I graduated high school, the "and then" of history—the study of cause and effect—had become my way of organizing the products of time.

One evening, he offered another take on the Vera tale, which bore little resemblance to the earlier fable.

We were in the living room. He was leaning back in his favorite recliner. The evening news was on. Something the anchor said—a story from the annals of the seemingly endless Cold War—struck him. Father pulled up and hunched forward, clearing his throat.

"You should know about Vera," he said.

In this account, Father claimed that Vera's husband, a hospital administrator, had actually bought her from her mother in a village near Kyiv. "For money?" I asked. "That's my point," he said. "People were poor." Vera's own husband had worked in various Soviet clinics around the country before finally landing, then losing, a position in Bucharest, Romania. Unemployed for some time, he'd avoided conscription into the Iron Guard—your friendly local Nazi group—and severed friendships with men he'd known since childhood. Eventually he fell off the back of an electric tram as it rounded the corner a few blocks from his home. There was a rumor he'd been pushed, but Vera never verified it. What good would it do, knowing her husband had been murdered? His death left Vera to raise her two sons alone.

"I thought you said she had three. Three sons."

"One died. Remember?"

"That was a true story? Come on, Dad. That was just how you got me to eat my peas."

The old man shook his head.

"But you were born in Kyiv."

"I may have been."

"May have been?"

"I was a boy. Everyone's dead. The facts are unclear."

Two sons. Three. Unclear? The facts didn't matter. Soon he'd be telling me Vera had never existed.

For the moment, though, the story was that at the start of the war Vera worked as a nurse in the asylum her husband once administered on the outskirts of Bucharest, raising her boys on its grounds. Countless people went mad in those years, and the facility was so overcrowded that patients slept two to a bed. Since many were incorrigible sex offenders, the nights were loud and violent, and sometimes not everyone returned for breakfast.

It seemed my great-aunt Vera had been a nurse in a hospital for the mad at a time when inmates ruled the world.

"Why are you telling me this now?" I asked.

"Somebody's got to know the story," he said.

A woman I dated in college accused me of having had a happy childhood. I took the charge seriously. I was then drifting in a bohemian milieu, and at that age neuroses and articulate despair were evidence of superiority and sophistication.

"But it all went bad," I protested, hoping to score points. Doesn't matter, I was told, it's the first six years that count.

I admit without shame: For a while—no matter how briefly—my childhood of beach plums and thorny bushes and biting winds and storms had been lit by the kind of wild light you find growing up by the sea, reared by two characters who had their differences but who knew how to take their pleasures, too. The lighthouse from Ten Pound Island glared nightly into the third floor of our triple-decker like that eye of God on a dollar bill. Ms. Johnson sang opera in amateur productions in Beverly, and many nights I'd fall asleep to arias from *Aida* or *Carmen* wafting up through the vents or open windows. And sometimes I would hear her standing on the back porch whistling Mimi's song from *La Boheme*, accompanied by foghorns. Our neighbor on the first floor wasn't so nice—he was a mechanic who drank, fought loudly with his girlfriend, and, as we found out when he was arrested, sold heroin to kids at the school up the street. But he never gave us any trouble because he respected Father, even feared him. The way all of us did, I suppose.

What we feared was all we didn't know about him, which as it turns out was just about everything.

Later, of course, I understood there were no water-walkers in my family, no miracle workers, no escape artists, and I see now that was a good thing. Because there were no waters to walk on in the first place. The Atlantic never freezes, at least not in New England. And miracles, I've found, take no work at all. They just happen, effortlessly—or else they don't.

The contradictions in Father's character made me believe I needed to understand him before I could love him. I was young. Only later—and why it took so long would require eons to tell—only later, too late for some things, did I learn that love has no prerequisites at all.

None.

ED PAVLIC

Definition of the Contemporary Reach

tell me baby, what's the matter now
aw, you trying to quit me baby, but you don't know how
—Billie Holiday

you can't keep track of what's what calling it what it's not   but

stir shade & heavy cream into coffee & there's breath-flash   clean
as knife-wind in the brain   blown down the full length
of the lake whipped into white waves   they break on broken

concrete slabs   ice ripples its hook-fingered rebar spine
    reinforced pearls
condense in the tight-curled down
parts of me wink in the hair of his forearm   the lake's black &
    pitched

on us in sheets that catch the flame of the city

in the air   as for air there's just enough for now   the doors of the
    car
frozen shut   & it's him it's not him   it's the taste of his voice
in my mouth   we talk every day till there's nothing to say   till no
    ache

polices his veins   till nothing ever ached   my mouth for his

& so never would   if it's now the battery's *been* dead   quiet
    storm
gone & tangled
around each other for warmth   the past's nothing if not the
    irregular
pulse
        of his lap in my ear   & that cop saunters & wags & pisses

on the car   &   thank christ   leaves   it was all there & now it's
    not
take the dice & let them kick
up on the curb   you can walk away before

they're still if you want   but don't tell me there's no number
on the ground   don't say the last breath can't be
the last   & after that it's not breath

till you've kicked the rear window out & let night be this

night & splash to life all on your face
which is this face that sounds that sounds like my hands
that ache beneath this ice   as for friends & love

& Berryman   two out of three

will tell you what to do with the present   a.k.a. chili con
    temporary: get
the frozen flame in your belly & your hipbones cross
to the wrong side of the rail gone raw   & wave goodbye

& yes   every weekend   Ric's grandmama   Ms. Lou   handed us
    her keys
to Chicago & told us: *remember baby, every goodbye ain't gone*

but sure as I've looked thru the keyholes   I'll be damned

                              if she ain't gone missing   too

The Battle of Anghiari

Boarding the local at Midtown, all seats taken,
he worked his way through the car with firm lean arm
from his black T-shirt pulling him down the high
stainless-steel handrail. Through that forest of bodies
flashed his teeth: in spasms his lips would pull back
and his eyes rage, then calm. Neat, perhaps thirty,
the self-enclosure of the others a gapped curtain
for his tic, the racket of the express
for a steeled moment harmonizing it.
Then a seat, and he sank into his paperback novel.
Leonardo had caught him in sketches, the head
twisting in red chalk over one shoulder yelling
some command, the neck's tendons wired, the carry
of that voice drowned by the long cacophony
and thus unheard anyway by those left standing,
the din still in their ears, they not yet home.

Brownfield Sonnets

1. Hay

What's the Latin word for hayfield? Virgil's
mum in his instructive *Georgics,* though
my neighbors talk of nothing but:
how weeks of cool rain forced the upright grass—
seed ready to burst from fuzzy heads
too wet to cut, releasing to the wind
goodness that should be stuffed above a stall,
or pulled by steers from round bales.

In Maine, 2005, a man can lose sleep
over the price of gas pitching Canada's
alfalfa out of reach. He can't walk away
from braying cattle; either he feeds or shocks
them up the trailer ramp, so many pounds
of flesh for here or to go, with golden fries.

2. Chickens

Virgil doesn't mention chickens either.
True, they're lower than goats
and maybe there's nothing to advise
but *freshen their water and feed.*
An oven-stuffer roaster's never sacrificed
to Jupiter or Pan; no eggs decorate
the altar. Chicks don't require breeding,
herdsmen, or a shepherdess. Left alone

with scratch for a week, they'll thrive;
a wash of roost paint smothers hen disease.
Yet why not praise the flock whose yield
is easier to get than milk or fleece,

their preening, companionable gabble funny,
the rooster's brag a brassy *sleepers, wake!*

3. Whose Woods These Are

I think I know the guy who backpacks up
to Patton's tract, tending his dope. He plants
between slash piles on paper company land,
the fresh clear-cut tilled by a skidder's chains.
Tree limbs, bulldozed like garbage at the dump,
baffle a helicopter's jittery light and lens;
and, sprayed with liquid soap, repel Bambi's
hungry muzzle. Mulched by duff, ditched,

fertilized—not long before stems topple
in dreadlock-headed flower. Like the raccoon
who smells ripe corn, husking every ear
of Silver Queen the night before my annual
Corn Boil, I'll snap the palm-tree fronds
unfurled like parasols, and bag his stash.

4. Mist

There's a place where Shepard River mist
crawls up the shady bank and over the road.
As you step through its otherworldly chill,
the spring-fed stream, rain-flushed, hurries
voices of the dead to Biddeford Pool,
so many notes colliding in one chord,
the pressure hurts your ears. You listen for
your mother's milk-paint recipe, Dad's worst

fish story—unsure what the bodiless discuss,
or how. Mosquitoes vibrate from the puddle
in the palm of every leaf, falsetto mob
at your collar crying for blood; you walk
a few feet into sun, where fog transpires
and mud, gumming your instep, cracks to dust.

El burro es un animal

Kids in the Dumb Class weren't allowed to enroll for French
So instead we learned the difference between *ser* and *estar.*

A yellow-haired midget father in a white suit cursed me for being
In his family tent-yard, where I had wandered. He was my size.

All a misunderstanding, we weren't that stupid. I was earning
Free tickets to the circus for helping set up chairs in the bigtop.

¿Es larga, la historia? The language of Cervantes and Góngora was
Suitable for *nosotros,* being *bobos.* There are two kinds of *being.*

Fidel Castro was staying at the Theresa Hotel in Harlem.
He brought live chickens to eat, because they were safe.

What *are* these fucking motherfucking kids doing here, God
Damn it to the son of a bitch fucking cocksucking Hell?

Ya las gaviotas abren sus alas para volar, the young swallows or gulls
Are opening their wings to fly. We were stupid. He was small.

He was a scowling angel all dressed in white, wingless, his hair,
I suppose it was dyed, like yellow candy over his pink forehead.

Was and was. When Salvador Allende was elected President, what
Was the name of that honorable general killed by the CIA?

Be the fucking Hell out of here you little shit sons of bitches, Jesus
Christ, before I put my foot up your goddamned fucking asses.

You are sick, the door is closed, María is tired, the apple is still green.
The apple is green, Juan is intelligent, she is serious, the story is long.

Tornado

The yellow eye and needle
beak of that black bird,
because the tree
is swaying—look,
it's saying *I,*
I'm staying.
Reports from the south
and west come far worse,
where of course they understand
the danger, who chose danger
in that form and not another,
though it must seem unfair,
disproportionate, how that balance
of gusts fired to gusts cooled
forms a stillness
whose terrible freight roars past
some houses, not others.

The Statue

As a child, as little more than an infant
still learning numbers and words, I went
to sleep after praying for uncles and aunts,
for the living and the dead, with one hand
in my mother's hand through the bars of the cot,
while I held in the other a bronze statuette
of Mary given to me by my godmother,

Sister Rose Teresa, to whom my mother
at the kitchen table wrote *Dear Rita,*
in the letters she sent across the ocean
—having copied into them my prayer
for the nuns, which she said they'd treasure,
since *a small boy's words fly to Heaven
and by the angels there are heard.*

So the night Sister Rose was discovered
in the convent bath, we subtracted her
from the living and added her to the dead,
my mother and I, before we prayed,
her hand in one hand, while in the other
I held Mary the Mother of God,
the statue given me by my godmother.

China Map

I was worn out, lost, and sixteen
in China at 6 p.m., everyone
suddenly in a purchasing frenzy,
when he stopped me with a smile
that just turned me upside down:
gold caps on one side, gaps on the other.
I could tell he was more human
than most people, or more kind.
He was old the way everyone is old
when you're sixteen: maybe fifty, or seventy.
I had passed through the village of pork,
the village of shoes, the village of cotton shirts
and linen. Each few blocks the commodity
changed, the sounds and smells trans-laundered
the air you walked in. He held out to me
a section of the oddly shaped fruit
with a rough, nubbly green rind,
smooth amber glistening inside,
a taste divine, beyond my tongue.
He was a busy man with buyers,
we were smack at the core of the village
of fruit. All of his globes were selling.
I was a ready target, fanning out
the colored bills, raising my brows.
He looked at my hotel's card,
looked into both of my eyes, as if to say
it was going to get dark fast,
and sat us down on two crates side by side,
and stopped his hawking then to draw,
in deft, meticulous detail, a map
to get me back: the splashing fountain
with the fish inside the osprey's mouth,
the statue of the sword-bearing giant,

the dog-legging street that led
to a cat's-paw alley just before the really
sharp turn. When he drew an intersection,
the stoplight had all three circles
with diagonal hyphens radiating out—
and that fountain! He spent a lot of time
making it sparkle on the paper bag
under his knife-sharpened, spit-greased pencil.
I remember his ropy hand veins working.
I remember this fruit I carried back
to my hotel and up the stairs, glowing and round
like the truth. Like the globe of the truth
of everything in the whole wide world.
I didn't know how to go about eating it
when I got back to my room:
no knife, no dish, no napkin.
I sat and watched it ripen in the dusk,
breathing its aroma, which seemed
the antidote to every wrong thing.
In the morning I can't believe I just
left it behind. That fruit.
Also, doubtless, the map.

Desperate to Get There Before the Light Fails

But as we rose from the café table in Trastevere
who could not help but notice
that it was as beautiful a day as could be imagined
in Rome: an early October afternoon in mid-July.

There's little you can't say against Rome,
from the infernal roar to the eternal siestas.
There are portents: the coppery-skinned woman
in the rusty dress with her hair still wet

at the bus stop at Largo Argentina;
message from Etruscan Central.
Italian cities are moody and capricious,
like a woman with a Pekinese on a wire coil we follow

to the cobbler and wait to replace a heel.
Minutes shy of siesta's end.
A couple, antsy, peering through the smudge-
interred window where they can discern

a beaded purse on a rail, a pair of men's
black shoes on a downward tilted shelf.
In the shop adjacent, a framer punches
a reproduction out of its gilded borders.

And in that dark and woody Furniture Repair
an apprentice, head down,
yellow rubber overalls,
matted black hair brushed forward, exits

while the old men recede
further and further into the dusty darkness.
No tone of lament.
What is there to begrudge?

The mid-afternoon light sweeps across the Tiber,
uncovering encrypted scrawls and encrusted designs
for an instant on the fortified banks—
then they're gone.

I follow it—light that startles
a steep, circuitous street, so that each
rundown façade stands out in its first color.
The subdued tints blend in this instant:

rapture of lavender against aquamarine against ochre
    against olive-gray against terra-cotta.
Masolini Masaccio Raphael.
Imponderable pale hues. Now broken.
Congestion. Stoplights. Con men.

But relief's in sight, the Aventine
where you can breathe—
In the park, on the stage of a children's theater,
kids are fencing with bright cardboard swords.

An old codger shakes a bitter, vituperative cane.
The righteous man.
Everyone shrugs, yeah, old people live in the past.
Under eerily clustered umbrella pines,

teens lounge cross-legged on the high parapets.
Backs to the city.
They're not afraid.
They won't fall.

TOMAŽ ŠALAMUN

The Man I Respected

When I came back from Mexico, I looked
like death. My mouth broke down,
weather-beaten. I was paying for my
sins, my palate had melted. I could touch
my brain directly with my tongue. It was
painful, terrible, and sweet. While Svetozar
was sitting outside, the cabinet of dental
instruments was crashing down. I brought down
the chest of instruments. No, I'm not precise,
he was leaving the examination room, I only had
a premonition who he was, I didn't even know him.
When I sat down my energy shattered the chest of
instruments. To shift from one world to the
other means an earthquake. Yesterday he died.

translated from the Slovenian
by Phillis Levin and the author

Southern Gothic

Poor white and pining, the full moon coins
its antebellum image on a welling tide
that rakes the shingle back across the bay.

A sight whose sounds summon into mind
the muffled ruckus of a million tiny
broadcast die caroming off green baize,

the bone-clatter by which fate decides
the youngest child in a family of nine
will be the first to die (the death marked

by an asterisk in the family Bible
that records such things) from illness,
or an overdose, or a traffic accident.

The Secrecy of Animals

You take the fragments of the world
and put them into boxes, each one
smaller than the last. Lock each one.

It's a kind of violence. The blue
triangles of your mother's dress, or
the birds that flew backwards that morning.

It was an unremarkable day.
Flat weather. Repeating cycles of traffic.
There was nothing to read.

What your husband said had adjectives and nouns.
You can see them from outer space.
Inside that box are cold animals.

Your hands are so far away, as when
the magician separates his assistant
into territories of herself.

No wind. Porcelain stars.
The name on your nametag
is unrecognizable.

My Other Grandmother

Her pale square face looks out like Fate—
through a dark kerchief clipped under her chin

with a narrow, elegant pin; you can make out
a white headband under her shawl; her jacket

and skirt cut from the same coarse dark cloth.
The uneven stitches of her hem hand-sewn—

dark leather men's shoes sticking out.
Yet her face has no coarseness—high cheekbones,

high forehead, small nose. Her narrow, suspicious eyes
don't give much away. The corners of her mouth

turn down almost in a sneer. Her private mind at work.

The closer you look, the younger she seems. Forty
dressed up to look sixty? She could be an actress

in a peasant costume—except for the rough
cloth of her thick hands, her long thick fingers in her lap

curling under her long thumb. Her hips seem broad,
but maybe the thick cloth makes her look heavy.

Her sons and daughters—one greedy; one
resigned to poverty and loose teeth; one fat and jolly; one

angry with the world—unfatherly, unmotherly (yet he could
still charm the ladies)—was it from her they

inherited their bitterness? Their charm? Their nerve?

Her only trace, this worn photo, crudely cut out
and pasted to a piece of cardboard.

My father must have carried it with him. Did he
ever hear a word from her *(could she write?)*—

or about her—after he left home; left Europe?
Did he know when she had died?

Her name was Leah—he never spoke of her.

DON SHARE

Food for Thought

Never weaned from anger
(the stars incline but do not require),
left alone she thinks hard

thoughts mean as snow
at harvest: home is paradise
to cats, hell for wives, she thinks,

are all babies slippery?
boys hate old men, but women
despise them: she thinks,

bed full of bones,

and bad usage
aggravates the matter

She had a smack of this disease—
like Vulcan he made creaking
shoes for his Venus,

that is to say, being blood-
thirsty, Nature turns leaves
red every single fall, and she thinks

love more violent

Even Noah, Jerome says,
"showed his nakedness in his
drunkenness

which for six hundred years
he had covered in his soberness."

So what can she do with his
scores of years for scruples?

The sailor doesn't see the water
passing underneath his ship;

the fisherman all the fish deep
in the sea around his nets—

So, she thinks, nothing
will ever be my own, not even time,
and feeds herself more thoughts

the way ravens fed Elijah:
invisible, invisible, invisible

Coelacanth

Once thought to be extinct...
lives at depths of up to 1,500 feet...
dies of shock when brought to the surface...
almost nothing is known about it...
—National Geographic

I saw you in a book: bubble-eyed and staring,
mouth spookily aglow with a sourceless yellow light.

Extinct, you cruised among cold silences
until a hand roughly hauled you out of your element,

and for a moment you lived, only to die again,
in shock at a world too bright, too dry, too thin.

Mute, you speak volumes: the weight of water pressing
on you like an enormous question, your ancient saucer eyes

peering, constantly peering, through ragged curtains of Time.
What, what do you see? *Oh tell me, tell me, tell me.*

You and I, we live in depths profound and ceaseless,
we swim against cold currents until, netted

and gasping, we are shocked to find out
not what we are, but what we have never been.

Conversation

1

He said it would always be what might have been,

a city about to happen, a city never completed,

one that disappeared with hardly a trace, inside

or beneath the outer city, making the outer one—

the one in which we spend our waking hours—

seem pointless and dull. It would always be

a city in the dark, a city so shy that it waited,

dreading the moment that was never to be.

2

I said that the dawning of the unknown

was always before us and that the realization

of anything is a constant threat. I also said

that there is sadness in knowing that the undoing

of what has been done will never take place,

that the history of now is as distant as the future

of when. Our skills are limited, our power

to imagine enfeebled, our cities doomed.

All roads lead to the malodorous sea.

The Earth

translated from the French by Anne Atik

Small crystal globe,
Earth's small globe,
Through you I see
My lovely glass bowl.

We're all locked up
In your hard strict breast
But so polished, so glossed
Rounded by light.

Like this horse running
Or a lady who halts
Or the flower on her dress
A child on its planet.

Or those sitting at a table
Or smoking a while,
Others lying on the sand or
Warming their hands at a fire

And we turn around ourselves
Without vertigo or strain
Like the sky, its stones
Like death we shine.

DEBORAH TALL

But in the Onset Come

Where is it, the semaphore branch or
bellwether sounding a trail over hill, dale, parking lot...
leaves down, birds vanished, only a left-over tic and shiver

while overhead roar the test flights, free-fall
shadows stippling the defunct garden
thick with invasives, those exogamous brides.

I ask for bread, someone hands me a
slaughtered goose, points to the stage-left exit
where the long dead wave from tinted windows.

There are dust rings around the stars, snow
that can't find its way to the ground,
old scripts curled in silver flame.

When it's time, when it's time,
I'll take off my watch
and listen for the tick

of bare tree limbs
batting at what once
I knew as sky.

Thetis on Achilles, The Son

Starts in estuary
          whelm and whirl of rock-skin,
     sea-swell, the hove called salt.
               I loved
the hero-to-be,
               his life first arrowed unto me,

                    scudding, spared, still
                    unconscious.

          No
                    he and *she* to wash
          away yet, my
inhale planked to his ex—.
               Plus our everywhere wet
                         trough
                              in the tidal
     waves repeating
               over and over.

Given, milky teats, realm of belly,
given, his body my body by faith.

Which to keep him I'd
               cozen, always,
guarding every
               waterway I owned.

See hand, heart, heel
               where I dipped him, to save.

See the would-be bargain,
               backridge of epic,

hovering in half-truths as if I really could
                    unwick what was to come.
In the end when they took him
             the spell of the world sang
       name, rank, date
of birth, your mother's
               maiden, your father's post.

Still, I said *no hands*
              out the window, boy,
    I said *no swimming*
             at the water's edge.
The sand's oozy blank
           is where they've got oblivion,
solistenyougetbackhererightnow.

Nothing worked. He wanted all the wrong
            toys, tanker's prow,
the true-edged sword, a golden set of spears.

And when it came to the armor, god-hammered, bronze
          through the beam,
             well, I never begged. Another
          exoskeleton, extra
skull. Though I'd made him perfect, zodiac'd
          to last.

Meanwhile, *time being,*
on that outline-horizon,
          you could see empire

serrated at the edges: junk boats,
             great ships,
the soldiers waving, even the geese
      defined in V's.

Soon each new sight needled,
   and Fame, that bitch, stuck

like a splinter inside him,
                   cutting the flesh

in whispers, rumoring,
          you can win, you can win.
                 With wood hewn
          like a beast at the door.

#33

The song of someone like me
                              begins on the penny whistle.
A few notes, just a few, up and down.
The bass line comes in,
                              then the lead and second guitar.
Brushstrokes on the snares.
And then the singer, Lord, then the singer steps up.
What voice could slip this backdrop?
Only the rise and fall of the newly damned, perhaps,
                              or the Great Speckled Bird.
Or some sough through the big larch limbs, some sibilance in
    the pines.
Little lost squawks in the natural world,
                                        lost voices.
I gather them unto me, I become their mouthpiece.

———

Sordello, with lazy and honest eyes, still waits for us
Beyond the *palude* off Via Mantovana
Just this side of Sabbionetta,
His terraced, invisible mountain
Rising above Lake Garda into the infinite.
Not time for that hike yet, we hoped,
                              feet hot on the cobblestones
In front of Palazzo Ducale.
Not yet, we hoped, our foreheads already feeling the sword's tip.
And angel wings.
                    You got to carry that weight for a long time,
And pray for the angel's wing
When the time comes, when the time does come.

———

Moonlight like watery paint
On the yard grass and arborvitae.

Shadows like Franz Kline from the spruce trees.

Circle of neighbor's basketball goal like the entrance to Hell
On stone-spattered, leaf-littered driveway.

October, old ghost month, you outline my *fine del cammin.*

———

There is a photograph of Stan Hyman and me in our Army
    dress blues,
2nd Lieutenants, standing in front of a No Parking sign
In Pacific Grove, California, 1958.
There are a hundred million snapshots
Just like it, Stan's wedding day, the 24 August.
Mine means a world to me, a world never to return,
But one never left, if truth be told.
And yours? You have at least one, I know, just like it,
                        different people, different place,
But the same. What does it mean to you?
Who could imagine it would ever become like this?

———

All I have left undone, I hope someone will make good
In this life or the next,
                    whichever comes first. Or second.

———

Moon riseth not, as some Victorian must have said back in the day,
Stars like a motorcycle's exhaust
Through the limp leaves of the maple trees.
                            Not much excitement here,
Though headlights and taillights go back and
Forth like pine-pitch torches in some Attic procession,
The limbs of Orpheus overhead
At the front,

his blue-tongued and pale head behind on the slow Rivanna,
Bumping from snag to sandbar, but singing, still singing.

———

The start of things, and the end of things,
Two unmarked graves,
                    the autumn wind rising west of the mountains.
Goodbye to the promise of What's Left.

———

The emptiness of nonbeing,
                    that which endures through all change—
Something to shoot for, for sure,
Something to seek out and walk on,
                              one footprint after the next.
In any case, after this life of who-knows-how-many-years,
Who's not a shrunken, pitiable sight?

———

I empty myself with light
Until I become morning.

Music Heard in Illness

"Everything changes but the avant-garde."
—Paul Valéry

A few words are left us from the beginning.
Thank you, God, for allowing me a little to think again this morning.

Touch my face, touch this scarred heart.

Here, touch this upturned face as wind as light.

So they labored for three or four decades
to turn the perfectly harmless word quietude
into a pejorative sneer.

Call no man happy until he has passed,
beyond pain,
the boundary of this life.

We were standing alone at the window when it started
to rain and Schumann quietly.

That imbecilic plastic hive of evil—

To

night, and you
turned

and said,
although you were not there, Night.

What do we know but this world.

And although I could not speak, I answered.

ADAM ZAGAJEWSKI

Long Street

translated from the Polish by Clare Cavanagh

Thankless street—little dry goods stores
like sentries in Napoleon's frozen army;
country people peer into shop windows and their reflections
gaze back at the dusty cars;
Long Street trudging slowly to the suburbs,
while the suburbs head for the center.
Lumbering trams groove the street,
scentless perfume shops furrow it,
and after rainstorms mud instead of manna;
a street of dwarves and giants, creaking bikes,
a street of small towns clustered
in one room, napping after lunch,
heads dropped on a soiled tablecloth,
and clerics tangled in long cassocks;
unsightly street—coal rises here in fall,
and in August the boredom of white heat.

This is where you spent your first years
in the proud Renaissance town,
you dashed to military drills and lectures
in your outsized overcoat—
and now you wonder, can
you restore the rapture
of those years, can you still
know so little and want so much,
and wait, and go to sleep so swiftly,
and wake adroitly
so as not to startle your last dream

despite the December dawn's darkness.
Street long as patience.
Street long as flight from a fire,
as a dream that never
ends.

Do Something

The soldiers keep Margaret in view. She carries her tripod, unsteadily, and an extra poncho for a bib. That they have let her come this far might be due to the weather, or possibly the kinds of amusements of which she remains unaware. Still, assume that they watch, tracking her as she stomps along the fence and positions herself by the sign that clearly states: *No Trespassing. Government Property. Photography Forbidden.*

It has turned a wet, wet September, everywhere raining so the leaves, black and slick, paste to the soles of her boots, or Caroline's: Wellingtons borrowed from the back of the hallway closet where earlier Harry watched as Margaret rummaged, wondering where she could possibly be going in such weather.

She turned, boot in hand.

"It's raining," he repeated.

Deaf at most decibels, Harry now cast his voice into the silence, as if hoping for an echo or a nod.

"Nowhere," she had said, because this is nowhere, or anywhere, or somewhere not particularly known: an hour's drive from Wilmington if you took the busy roads, and then country, mostly, the drizzle graying the already gray landscape. Ye olde *et cetera*—cornfields, silos, a ravaged billboard for Daniel's peas, fresh from California, though this is technically Delaware and the land of soybeans. Ducks, too, the fall season in full swing; the drizzle split by the crack crack crack of the hunters' guns.

She parked near the drainage ditch that edges the fence, chain link, as if for dogs, though there are no dogs here, only a guard tower, a landing field, and the soldiers who wait for the planes. But that isn't right, exactly. The place is vast, a city of a place, with barracks—are those called barracks?—and trucks and cul-de-sacs and no doubt children sleeping, Army brats—or is this Marines?—in the two-story housing labyrinth not so far from where she gets out, near the drainage ditch, near the landing field, near the place where the plane will descend. This she knows. The rest—the presence of children, the numbers involved, the ranking, the hierarchy—she truthfully has no idea.

Margaret skewers the tripod in the mud and adjusts the poncho to cover her. Today, she plans to bite skin. She can almost taste it: the salt of it, the flesh; see herself in her resistance: Margaret Morrisey, mother to Caroline and the dead one, James; wife to Harry. She mounts the camera on the track and angles the lens toward where the plane will descend—they come from the east, she has learned, out of Mecca, the bodies mostly wrapped in flags but sometimes carried in a tiny box.

"Christ, Mother," Caroline said after the first arrest, the fine. "Get a life."

"Your great-great-grandfather ate horse feed; that was his dinner. He'd soften the oats with spit. He came to this country for food. Literally."

"Apropos of...?" Caroline said.

"It meant something," Margaret said. "America."

"It's illegal."

"This is a free country."

"Please," Caroline said.

The two sat at Caroline's kitchen table, Caroline in one of her suits meant for business, her cigarette burning in the misshapen ashtray a ten-year-old James had spun out of clay. Caroline's children were elsewhere, having reached the age of the disappeared—their voices shouting orders from behind the locked doors of their bedrooms or even standing present, their bodies imperfect, studded casts of their former selves; if they were somewhere within them they were very, very deep.

"I should never have told you I voted for him," Caroline said.

"I would have guessed."

"The rules have to do with respect," Caroline said. "Or something. Anyway, they're the rules. It's law. Besides, it's none of our business. None of your business."

"Says whom?" Margaret said, to which Caroline had some sort of reply.

Margaret listened for a while, and then she did not; she thought of other things, how she would like to have believed that not so long ago Caroline would have stood beside her at the fence, that her daughter would have carried a sign or at least shouted an obscenity. But this was before Caroline took that job in the Financial District. The Fucked District, she calls it, but the money's good, she says. It's serious money.

"Mother?"

"I was listening," Margaret said.

"Forget it," Caroline said. She tapped her nails, those nails, on the table, then the buzzer rang—delivery—and the conversation ended.

"Dinnertime," she yelled in the direction of the doors.

Crack. Crack. Crack.

The men have had enough. They climb down from their tower to slog through duck country, technically Delaware, the first state, though most have trouble with the history; one can hear their boots, or is that frogs? The sucking. Soon enough they'll reach her. Margaret records their magnified approach; records them unlocking the gate and stepping to the other side, records their blank expressions. The trouble is she can only pretend to hate them.

"Good morning, Mrs. Morrisey." This from the one Margaret calls Tweedle-Dee.

She straightens up, adjusts the poncho.

"We'll remind you that you're trespassing. That taking photographs is forbidden."

"Today," she says, hand on tripod, "I plan to resist."

Their arms remain folded. Four pair, as usual; a pack; a team; a unit, perhaps, or would they be a regiment? No, a regiment is bigger, a regiment is many. She tries to remember from soldier days, from mornings James explained the exact order of things— sergeant to lieutenant to captain to king—his miniature warriors arranged throughout the house in oddly purposeful groupings. She would find them everywhere, assaulting a sock, scaling the ping-pong table, plastic, molded men with clearly defined weaponry and indistinct faces. When she banished them to his room, fearing someone would break a neck, James had cried and cried.

"That would be more than your usual fine, Mrs. Morrisey."

He is a horse's ass, but then again, a boy once James's age who should be pitied.

"I plan to resist," she repeats. One of the Mute Ones has his hand out as if to help her across the muddy plain. They are waiting, she knows, for Margaret to do something. Collapse, she thinks, then does, more a buckle than a collapse, knowing full well the ridiculousness of it, how small she'll become. The big one bends down to help her. *Now,* she thinks, though it is not until it is done that she understands she has found the courage to do it, biting the soft part of that hand, the hammock of skin between thumb and forefinger.

Caroline sits next to Harry in the detention waiting room (she must have taken the train!), no question who's the boss. Our girl could split atoms, Harry once said. We ought to lease her to GE.

Sorry, darling, Margaret mouths to him. He looks at her with his doggy yellow eyes; then Caroline leads them both out.

In the sunshine they blink: "Look at the weather!" Margaret says, reflexively. "What a treat!"

Caroline has opened the car door.

"Get in," she says.

They sit in silence to home, the radio punched to static and static and static then punched off, again, then the familiar drive, the front door, the hallway, the kitchen. Caroline makes tea and calls a Family Meeting. There's a hole in the place where James would have been so Margaret steps in and wanders around while Caroline speaks of Responsibility and Reputation and Appropriate Behavior, and, yes, the Germs in your Mouth, and Patriotism, but mostly, mostly, mostly, Mother, Embarrassment.

"Please," Caroline says. "I'm at wit's end."

Margaret would like to cradle Caroline in her arms, Caroline sleepy and hatted and a bit jaundice yellow, but she cannot. Caroline has grown; she's taller than Margaret and twice divorced and a millionaire, she has confessed. A mill-ion-aire, she said.

"Where are your friends, Mother?" Caroline asks.

Margaret shrugs. She hasn't thought of friends recently, nor her standing Wednesday at Sheer Perfection; her hair's gone shaggy and gray and her cuticles have grown over their moons.

"I'm sorry, darling," she says. "I'll stop."

How has it come to this? There was Youth, Margaret thinks.

Then, Love: A certain indefatigable, copper-colored Spirit. Wasn't she the one who had convinced Harry to do a U-turn on the GW Bridge? And what of Leonard Nan's retirement? She'd worn a blond wig and pharmaceutical pearls, hula-hooped her toast gyrating the thing to her knees. She used to leave it all to chance, or Certain Men, actually. Wasn't she the one with the Robert Kennedy dartboard? Didn't she support Nixon to the finish?

Now she is blindsided by fury; the tide of her anger rising at certain unpredictable moments (yes, the *tide*), as if drawn by an internal moon, waxing and waning, though mostly waning.

A disclaimer, first: she lost no one in The Tragedy, no Hero her James, just an ordinary mortal, his (by inference) an unheroic death: cancer of the blood—blah blah blah—one cell fried—blah—and then another—blah blah—until nothing remained but bone and sinew, James's lungs mechanically pumping, a ring of them singing before they turned off the machine. Godspeed. And the machine stopped. Godspeed. Which is not to say she didn't know someone who knew someone; which is not to say she forgets we are living under the Cloud of It, that there are Reliable Threats, that Evil Lurks, that there are those who seek to undermine our Way of Life.

Yet if asked she will say James's death was her 9/11.

"We all have our very own," she'll say. "Don't you agree?"

Crack. Crack. Crack.

The next time Tweedle-Dee steps away from the others, approaching alone, the Big One with the bandaged hand hanging back as if on lookout.

"Did it hurt?" she calls to him. "Am I toxic? Infectious?"

"I'll ask you to read the sign, Mrs. Morrisey," says Tweedle-Dee.

"It's a free country," Margaret says.

"Not exactly," he says. Clearly there's a manual on How to Speak to the Protesters and/or The Criminally Insane.

"I'm not interested in the bodies," she says. "It's the wildlife I'm after."

"Camera's forbidden," he says.

He stands, square and sharp against the autumnal reds, his camouflage humorless, stuck in the sole season of winter. If she could see his eyes she predicts she would see embarrassment there, but they remain mirrored lenses, and anyway she is wrong: he is doing his job.

"Glorious day," she says, but he doesn't bite.

"So you can shoot them but you can't photograph them? I find that ridiculous. Ridiculous," she calls out to the Big One. "Does it still hurt?"

She grips the camera with her dirty fingers, though it is looped around her neck and going nowhere.

"You're trespassing, Mrs. Morrisey. This is Government Property."

She plunks down in Tweedle-Dee's shadow, her arms crossed.

"In Sweden there's no such thing," she says, squinting up. "You can camp anywhere. It's allowed. You could take a walk across the entire country if you wanted and no one could say, private property. I'd call that democracy, wouldn't you?"

He looms over her like a man mountain—trees and shrubs the pattern—his mirrored glasses the stone at the top, the place of the vista that from a distance could be snow, or water; bright, regardless, in the glaring sun. She waits as he gestures to the Mute Ones, to the Big One with the bandaged hand. They are all tired of her, it's clear, and bored. They step forward, unlocking their handcuffs, clicking and unclicking as if they'd rather be elsewhere. Even Tweedle-Dee wipes his forehead in an exhausted, parched gesture. She thinks of how he sees himself now, how he *pictures* himself—soldier or statesman—protecting the all of us from God knows what: Nothing; everything: An old woman with a camera. He protects is all, he's like a postage stamp or a flag; a symbol bought and sold, something with an adhesive strip to stick on an automobile bumper or football helmet—thirty-seven cents or a dollar ten in the big bin at Rite Aid.

The handcuffs are tighter than she would have imagined, and she finds herself humming the only song she can think to hum: "Amazing Grace," knowing, even while humming, how ridiculous she sounds, how outdated it's become, even quaint: Peace. She thinks to mention this to Caroline, to somehow explain: What she is trying to do is to aim for something real, she'll tell her, something that is not just an approximation of real.

Here the two of us, she'll say, the all of us: the soldiers, the protestor, were all from a scene already enacted; so that even my own inclination to *be*—

Caroline interrupts. "To what?"

The fine has already been paid, though this time they finger-printed—"Ma'am," Tweedle-Dee had said to Caroline. "Tell your mother to keep her mouth shut."

Be, Margaret says now. "To *be.*"

"Or not," says the Millionaire.

"When did everything stop being real?" Margaret says.

"Don't bring James into it."

"He would have—"

Caroline plugs her ears; she might be eight, again: a girl in braids and knee socks, six missing teeth so that she could no more blow a bubble than recite Pope, though James, a teacher at heart, had tried for weeks.

"I don't care, Mother. I mean, I do, but at some point you have to put yourself first."

"Like hell."

"What?" Caroline unplugs her ears.

"I said, I know."

"You know what?"

"I know you don't care."

The bubble burst, the lopsided attempt. James picked it himself out of Caroline's braids, though Margaret had still given him a scolding and threatened the back side of the hairbrush. James put it all in his Feelings Jar, a jar that, in its earlier life, contained dill pickles.

I was just trying to DO SOMETHING. I was just trying to teach her how to blow bubbles and you got so mad you could spit.

"I am just trying to Do Something," Margaret says, though Caroline is busy looking for dinner inspiration, for anything other than pasta. "You don't care to understand. It's like every-thing. Conversation, for example, is now just approximations of opinions adopted from other opinions that were approximations of opinions, *et cetera, et cetera.* I'm just trying to be real when everything is an approximation."

But this is not true, exactly. Death is not an approximation. It is completely real; it is unchangeable, forever—an approximation of nothing. Hadn't she seen it that first time she'd found the base, the barracks, the military galaxy? Where had she been going? She can't remember anymore. She was lost, she knew, had taken to driving, punching the radio to listen to men and women discussing God knows what, anything to drown out her own inside voice. Use your inside voice, she used to tell the children, meaning quiet. Softly. Hers shouted now; tore its hair.

She had followed the convoy of jeeps, had stopped across the highway with the other cars, curious at the rows and rows of them idling like so many school buses by the chain-link fence that surrounded the complex of guard towers and apartments and houses and a post office there in the middle of nowhere, or everywhere: soybean fields, corn crops, a V of geese heading south and somewhere else, just beyond, an abandoned barn where starlings roost in rotted eaves and a boy necks or smokes or pings his pocketful of stones one by one against the glass, wanting breakage: all boys do. At the center sat the plane, exceedingly complicated, wings folded and a scissored tail—more like a jackknife than anything that could fly—and from it soldiers transporting bodies, their families there to receive them, to take them back as real, as dead.

"This is no approximation," Margaret says. "This is what that idiot has the audacity to hide: the one thing true in the mess of it," she says, attempting to name it all for Caroline, who some time ago surrendered, running the sauce jar under hot water, her back to Margaret though presumably listening.

Now she turns, her hand dripping.

"I hear you, Mother," she says, popping the lid; she forks a noodle from the boiling pot and holds it out to Margaret. "Finito?" she asks.

Margaret dreams of James. In this one he steps out of the Cape Cod surf (those were the years!) wet and gleaming; he is as he was, a young man, a boy who loved books, who copied passages in letters to his mother, certain things he believed she might like, understanding her taste, he once wrote, in these matters.

Dear Mother, his name is Professor Burns, which is ironic, because he smokes like a chimney and even when not keeps the cigarette, somehow lit, behind his ear. There's a rumor his hair once caught on fire and he lost his place in his notes and for the rest of the semester kept one step ahead of the syllabus oblivious. He is a little odd, but I like him and this is my favorite class. I don't know if I love romantic poetry or just love the way he talks about romantic poetry.

I don't know if I just love that anyone can talk about romantic poetry at all how many years later and still weep. Yes, he weeps. Or did the other day after his lecture on Wordsworth. A few of the girls went up to console him; maybe it was just a ploy (ha ha).

Here he is! Margaret thinks in her dream. Look, here he is! He's been swimming—that scamp—all along!

She hears the waves roll out behind him, the crash of it so clearly. She is fearful he might decide to return to that riptide; how often has she warned him it could carry you for miles! But, no. He walks toward her, the sun behind him dazzling. He is a dazzling boy, a young man of promise without a single broken bone, nothing to be mended, stitched; strong-hearted. He takes no medications, she could tell you, and on that repeatedly filled-out form that has so many boxes in which to check yes he checks no, no, no, no! every time. He is no more an approximation than a red tulip in May, and here is the great joke of it: He is Real!

A delicious pain, almost sexual, wakes her. It is the great cruel trick of the night: to wake alone, regardless. She can scream or cry if she wants—Caroline's gone home, and Harry is deaf asleep, long in the habit of covering his eyes with a towel to block the light. She elbow-props herself to watch him breathe, he the father of her children, the great love of her life. He floats into outer space in his bubble. It will burst, eventually, and he, like the rest of them, will be gone.

To where?

An approximation of this, perhaps, or the curl of a shell, the color of leaves, a gesture; here but somewhere deep within.

James had once asked her what she believed; this toward the end of him, she remembers, or close enough. And she might have lied; she might have given her boy something more.

"Nothing," she had said, already furious. "Absolutely nothing."

He sat in the chair by the window. She had brought a blue shawl and oatmeal cookies she would set by the door for visitors.

"You're an original, Mom. I've meant to tell you," he said.

"Thank you, darling," she said, wanting to hear more and wanting him to stop. She stood by the edge of his bed; she liked to stand there. She even liked this room, or well enough, on the quiet floor, with its view over the low rooftops to the sliver of river when the light went right, which happened more often now, in this season.

It had been autumn; the sun low, at a slant. That she found it too difficult to look at him she couldn't explain.

"And I forgive you your trespasses," he said.

"Hallelujah," she said.

If she had looked she would have noticed the blueness of the shawl, how odd to see him wrapped in blue.

"I hope you're wrong," he said.

"It wouldn't be the first time."

"If you are, I'll come back and rattle the windows," he said. "Think of it as my 'so there.'"

The windows more than rattle; so there. The wind more than blows. And somewhere else the terrified children must listen for what else—the cavalry, the infantry, the artillery—what had James taught her? Nothing. Everything. The names run together to a pooled point, the way blood will when the heart stops beating, when the machine stops. The machine stopped.

That she gets out of bed and dresses is almost beside the point. She no longer needs to write a note. She throws on loose clothing and goes, forgetting her empty camera—It was just like in the movies! she told Caroline. The soldiers rolled out the film and flung it in the garbage! They called her bite his wound!—forgetting her purse, backing the station wagon out the long drive to swerve down the once-dirt road toward the highway. At this hour there's little traffic, and she can speed as much as she likes, the cornfields and rows of soybeans saluting as she passes; in the end her only ally, the landscape, the actual black dirt of the country. Government property, my ass, she thinks.

Her headlights flood the woods she turns into: wild, brush grown, skunk cabbage in the hollows and arrowheads to be found; the all of it disturbed by this strange, Halloween wind. There might be children behind the trees, trick-or-treaters, Frankensteins and ghosts and ghouls shaking the skinny limbs of the aspen saying, I'm here! No, here! But they'd be flushed out, of course, by her, by the klieg lights on the landing field: in case of emergencies, no doubt: the jackknife slicing the air into ribbons, the families the only witness to the dead.

And what had she planned, anyway? To whom would she have shown her pictures? Harry? Caroline? Absent friends?

She parks near the guard tower and slams the door. The steel lattice work seems to glow in the moonlight, rising to the little booth of their tree-house watch. She might see breath on the glass, it is that cold and not so far up, or frost; she knows he is in there and she could find him if she climbed.

When did it become the boy she is after?

Does a radio play? Does he write a letter home? She wants to know where he's from, what he studied in school. She's interested in his early artwork, she could tell him. Elementary. Preschool, even. Did he begin with circles? Those circles! And then slowly, no; she had seen it in her children and her children's friends and her grandchildren, even. The loss of circles, eventually. Don't despair, she could tell him. It happens to everyone.

She would like to know where he sat in the cafeteria—with the popular children or off a little by himself, like her James, his sandwich crushed from his book bag, a tuna fish on white bread or maybe peanut butter. Did his mother include notes? An *I love you*, or *Hi, Handsome!* Perhaps he was not a son who required encouragement; perhaps he did fine on his own. His were not elaborate tastes—she can guess this—nor particularly demanding. He seemed fine with what he got until he wasn't; and when he wasn't he didn't complain. He made plans—how to leave, how to get out, how to make do, survive.

Was he interested in trains? Did he play a musical instrument?

Margaret stands at the fence looking in. The worst thing, she would tell him, is that she can no longer distinguish stars; when I think I have found one it moves out of view, just metal in orbit or a transportation vehicle. There are no longer fixed points by which to determine my direction, she would tell him. How can I ever again make a wish?

You are not responsible, she would say. It is shameful what we've done to you. We should all of us be ashamed.

"You are just like the rest of us," she says. "You are only trying to Do Something."

Does Margaret shout this or whisper? It no longer matters. She is suddenly tired and aware that she should go. She'll return home the way she came, driving back through ye olde *et cetera* to her rightful place beside Harry: Margaret Morrisey, mother to Caroline and the dead one, James.

Hormones, she'll tell Caroline, by way of explanation.

I miss him, too, Caroline will say, by way of apology.

"Goodbye," Margaret calls to them, though none can hear for the crack crack crack; the hunters particularly ravenous at dawn.

DAVID WEISS

Cry Baby

a novel excerpt

She lost me as the nation was losing Richard Nixon, good rid-
dance, whose head bobbled on his neck like a newborn's, as
mine would have, but whose five o'clock shadow was like the truth
coming out. A loss to no one but himself.

She sought for me early in the Ford administration right up
until the final collapse of the South Vietnamese army. Until finding was just another form of losing. Finders weepers, losers keep-
ers. That's the bitch of it. That's the précis.

Oh. Let me add: this was while she was still living with Dad.
With Pop. Horde father. Chromosome delivery system. Sky-god.
Putz.

There she'd be at the Grand Union, trolling the aisles, highway-
long and -wide, the banks of neon grinning down, the shelves
stocked to the gills, enough there to feed a conscripted army, and
she shopping to cook for two. Two chops. Two potatoes. The cans
of creamed corn. She put two in her cart. She couldn't wait to buy
three. She wanted three of everything. Two didn't lead anywhere.
She already knew that from her two years of marriage. Two wasn't
enough. Three was just right. Stable as a tripod. There were three
bears, three little pigs. The blind mice, troublingly, also came in
threes. But there'd been Churchill, Roosevelt, and Stalin at Yalta.
There were the Supremes. The Three Musketeers. The Three
Stooges. After all, every atom had at least a proton, a neutron, and
an electron. Only hydrogen had just the proton and electron. And
look what they did with hydrogen! Two meant competition or
combat. Yanks and Dodgers. Jews and Arabs. Jacob and Esau. U.S.
and U.S.S.R. If two didn't lead to three, well, you might as well let
the inventory on the shelves dwindle down to nothing. What
would be the point? What good were Mary and Joseph, Sarah and
Abraham, by themselves? Soon, though, there'd be three. I was
waiting in the wings, putting the finishing touches on, the wild

card, the one to give the story legs. Two was purely us versus them, tug o' war.

All except for the fish. Those two water breathers were different.

The fishbowl she'd bought was filled with colored pebbles and plastic pickerelweed and a sunken vessel lying brightly on its side in the clear, cool water. Bubbles burbled up from the bottom and made a lively sound. And the goldfish, the pair of them, more orange than gold, translucent creamsicle orange, marbled white in patches, had seemed to stare at her and make kissing or speaking movements (or gasping ones, it seemed to me). They were so intent on communicating.

She had noticed them in the pet store window on Linden Avenue; some expectancy in them, perhaps not unlike her own expectant condition, as they faced into the sunlight flooding through the plate glass, flagged her down. She wanted them to make that kind of contact with me, her little guppy, as she was wont to silently call me. Placed beside the bassinet, these fish, she hoped, would be my first guides to this life, colorful and gleaming, because life outside was going to be that way for me, for anyone with get-up-and-go, although it hadn't been and wasn't that way for her, but it could be for others, for her child, why not? After all, this was the age of affluence, however turbulent; even the used cars looked new, buffed to a sheen beneath the colored banners in the used-car lots. People were trading in their perfectly good cars to buy even newer, even spiffier Chevys and Lincolns and, now, Datsuns, compliments of the war machine, no longer in full swing.

These fish, Goldie and Locks, as she called them—"Why not Bagel and Lox?" said my thunderer-never-to-be—were going to be my introduction to the new and the hopeful, to buoyant possibilities the past could not weigh down; the dazzling turquoise and magenta pebbles like a treasure themselves suggested as much. When at last I was in my crib, I was sure to like them, my boon companions; already undulating their diaphanous fins to hold steady in the weightlessness of water, the fish mouthed silent words against the glass.

On her knees, she would bring her face right up to the bowl, and they would hover there as far apart as her left eye was from her right. It was like looking at a single being that had split into two, left brain and right brain, and she would listen as they declaimed directly through her to me.

And what, exactly, did they have to say? I'm inclined to answer, consult your own goldfish. The fact is, they say whatever you're hoping to hear. Besides, you can puzzle it out for yourselves. The options are less than infinite. For either they said: Hello, watery brother, it's a safe and lovely place you're floating in. Stay put! Enjoy it while you can.

Or they said: Face it, pal, you'll be leaving your fishbowl soon, but don't worry, you're just emerging into a bigger one, regrettably lacking in H_2O, it's true. But take solace in the fact that it's all being arranged just for you, although, be prepared, it may not be up to your present standards. Well, you'll know what a pair of lungs are for then.

Or they said: O brother, lucky the man who can escape the confines of his narrow sphere for long is the road and wide the horizon, and those into whose care you've been placed will prefer you to stay near them. They will change your water and your gravel and your filter toward this end. But with your two legs on the ground and your head in the clouds, you were made to wander and even to lose your way, to forget, and like the winged seed of the maple tree to ride the lazy convections of air upward and to settle after long drifting into some storm drain or puddled pothole.

They actually spoke that way, these fish, though what specifically they said I'm not, frankly, at liberty to divulge. You can be certain, however, that what she heard had an "all right, boys and girls!" insistent kind of cheeriness to it. She couldn't make up her mind if she wanted them to cheerlead or instruct me. Buck me up or cushion the blows. She wanted the world to be my oyster (whatever that meant), but all she had was her own life to go on. Thus, the fish were spokesfish for a future she had no personal belief in (though she had plenty of impersonal beliefs).

As far as I could make out from their charades-like gestures, though, the future was grim. Or rather, the future was like an unbarbed hook baited with a plastic worm rubbed in real worm guts. How little we are fed, their fishy mouths mimed, how little this aerated zone sustains our aspirations, though the flakes that drizzle down are sufficient to maintain our metabolic life which seeks nothing more than its own continuance. The habits of habitat do not a habitation make, they iterated in their arch theatric way, gaping wide their eating holes with the sort of exaggerated motions that those who whisper across a public space comically resort to. They made their message clear, at any rate.

Kneeling, she soothed the skintight eggplant of her belly with an absent-minded circular stroking and listened intently to every last eloquent word she wished the fish to say. No matter how darkly I understood their spiel and patter, the laying on of her hands was an unequivocal solace to me. Less a sentimental than a sensual education I was getting. One of the secrets of mother love.

*

Long before she did, I could feel them beginning, the contractions.

They began as the softest of embraces. A faint tightening as of arms wrapped around me. A lovely snugness so subtle that you couldn't tell if it were anything at all like the call you thought you'd heard and, listening hard in the silence, couldn't make out. Like being out playing with your friends. You think you hear your mom calling your name and then the shout, "Dinnertime!" You stop running, and all you can hear is your own panting and blood in your ears. There you are, sweaty and winded, uncertain whether you ought to go home, you don't want to, but you don't want to get in trouble, either. And now you're by yourself, and you're standing on the sidewalk; they don't seem to miss you, your friends; you strain to hear it again, the sound of your name, which, truth be told, you like to hear called, love her claim on you and that proprietary right to your attention and obedience, which no one else has, not even that placeholder, the law-giver, whose call has in it the whiff of threat which itself has in it the hint of force while your mom's has, no matter how exasperated it can get, a small bit of pleading as though the choice in the end were yours, though you have never chosen otherwise. You stand there by the curb in the heavy and loaded silence listening for corroboration of the call you may have only imagined you heard, hoping to hear it again and so unequivocally that you will be freed of your will and its cascading consequences, ready to run home, if only you actually hear it, with all your might and heart. That's how faint it was.

And here it was again, a whispery temblor, this time a squeeze more than a call, like a soft, meaty, two-handed, funeral-home handclasp meant to convey what a pleasure it is to meet you after all this time, I've heard so much about you, the squeeze like an arm around the shoulder to express concern, condolence, sorrow for your loss, that soft massage of the trapezius muscles that says, *I'm with you, buddy, my heart goes out, I feel your pain, the flowers are beautiful, understated and dignified, the service just right, captures the spirit of the man, beautiful and worthy, God is great and good, magnified be his name and sanctified, too, while we're at it, and blessed and praised and raised and honored and lauded, it's not about you, buddy, it's about the nation and its God, remember that in your grief.*

Oh, it was sweet. The long, slow pulse of it and the letting go. Rhythmic as rollers the contractions were, rolling in from Malta or the Moluccas, moon-summoned. Here it was, this time, clearer now, as if whispered into my ear alone like a Siren song, mouthing my was and my will-be, a call which I heard in the marrow of my bones, it came to me from within, it seemed, and I didn't have to go to it, I was it, already there in the making dark where the call was calling from, there at the bottom of the well, a living stone curled up in the amniotic waters, I was the song itself, the song the singing sang, a song whose single syllable left nothing out, told in the meter of contracting and expansion, an epic of creation and its raging outcomes.

It is sweet, too, at first, for her. A little early, near but not full-term, not to the day, surprising, really; she hasn't been expecting it yet, shocking and thrilling. She is ready, yet not ready, alone in the apartment, which is quiet, that fresh August quiet of a hot day starting off cool, the bubbler in the fishbowl inaudible from where she is, in the kitchen, by the stove, scrubbing with a Brillo pad at something burned onto the white enamel by the right front burner, the one she uses most frequently. She stops what she's doing, stops humming the refrain, *"Our house is a very, very, very fine house,"* which she can't get out of her head, places her fingertips down lightly on the smooth, shiny surface of the stove to steady herself. She can hear the wall clock tick. She can hear a shout from the street below, some kid, which normally fills her with an unaccountable happiness, the energy of it. All at once they belong, those sounds, to another world. She is all attentive cessation. She feels seized hold of, in the grip. It is a thing that takes precedence, a force that makes the day, the dailiness of day, give way. This is no longer Braxton-Hicks. No longer the body practicing.

Labor, she says to herself. *Labor pains.* The words try to acclimatize to the thing. But it's an experience, she can tell, that will not really or readily fit itself into words. Her body will not let it go. It will not let go of her body. It will not desubstantiate into the paleness of words. Meaning: it will always be hers. And then it releases her. The contraction is over. She makes herself finish the scrubbing. She forces the momentous back into its jack-in-the-box. She looks around at the ordinariness, the obliviousness of the ordinary, the salt and pepper shakers standing side by side, the cut-glass sugar bowl, the potholder on its wall hook, the cookie jar on the table in the shape of a jovial Dutch housefrau, hands on hips, whose body, whose pregnant body, she realizes, is the jar itself, full of the Oreos that Frank likes to crush in a glass of milk and eat with a spoon when he comes home from work. I have a cookie inside me, she thinks, almost giggly, and then the next contraction comes. No, not a cookie. Not a cookie at all. She leans against the doorjamb and strokes the beer-belly curve of her stomach, catching a finger on the popped-out belly button. Inside her is someone attached to her by its own umbilicus. The line is open. Like those waxed paper cups attached to a string children play telephone with. She thinks of the great chain of umbilical cords through which the first mother is, somehow, still attached to her, and that the cord must be cut, that hers was and her child's will be cut. And what sharp instrument do they cut it with? she wonders. Then, before the next one starts, she telephones her mother.

No answer.

She dials her doctor's office. Gets a busy signal.

She rings her sister, whose own son has just turned one two weeks before. Her sister. Her house-proud and hubby-proud and baby-proud sister. Who can't help but show off. Who can't help but squint at others who seem shadowy, less real, certainly less central, than she is, consigned to the shadows. Her sister, nevertheless.

No answer.

She rings Frank at work. Out picking up some wringer washers, she's told. Don't know when he'll be back. Wanna leave a message, Maddy?

Maddy. No one calls her Maddy. She's always been Madeleine. Hasn't permitted any diminutive.

The doctor's office is still busy. She dials it again. Busy. Redials. Busy. Busy. Busy. She goes from room to room deliberately as if the ground were far below her feet and she is tightrope walking on the thinnest wire. And then, her water bursts, gushing down her legs, soaking her slippers, darkening the rug.

She makes her way downstairs to her friend Phyllis, in 3C, stopping mid-step for her third contraction, a hand on the banister, a hand on the wall. Phyllis who is always in, always, it seems, on the phone, always fervently and loudly on the phone, who invariably opens the door with a nod and a roll of her eyes yet without missing a conversational beat, is out. She keeps her finger pressed to the nipple of the anemic bell.

Back in the apartment, she sits in the armchair beside the fishbowl and, uncertain what to do, it feels so odd to do nothing, switches on the TV. After all, she has already packed a small travel bag in the event, although there is not much in it, just some clothes, but which ones had perplexed her; everything she's been wearing for months have been *maternity clothes*. She won't have to dress for two anymore once they are really two. She could hardly imagine it, my little mug. *Sheyna punim.* And makeup? A nail file? What for? She had thrown in a hairbrush and a folding toothbrush. And panties, from the back of the drawer.

Through the squint of her fourth contraction, she watches the president, a man whose voice and quivery face she has come to loathe, everything with her these days is visceral, appear on the screen to say goodbye to his White House cabinet and staff, who have been gathered for the event. Has he really, finally, resigned, she wonders, as surprised by this as she was a moment before by the first pang of labor. *Mistakes, yes,* he is saying, his too-large head nodding. *But for personal gain, never,* his jowls shaking with a Parkinson-like tremble, alcoholic if you ask me. And now he is telling the assembled that his mother was a saint. *And I think of her, two boys dying of tuberculosis . . . and seeing each of them*

die... Yes, he is saying, *she will have no books written about her.*
Madeleine rubs the hard sides of her belly.

"Oh, sweetie," she says aloud, looking at him, talking to me.
She is quietly elated. She feels this day, this day of my birth, is
being marked, anointed, anchored to a moment of conspicuous
importance in the frothing sea of her nation's history. An end to
something is taking place that is also, for us, a beginning. And
though there is no other kind of end, what she feels is that something good can come out of this. She and I are a sign, are we not,
that history is not just murderous deeds disguised by lies masked
in high-minded, sententious talk. History is not just a steam-
roller. It comes again, the little seizure, and she feels it as a sweet
thing, and as fear, too, as worry, as the unknown. But now she
feels something historical, not just private, is going on inside her.
As if she were giving rise to the new, to the epoch-changing. Only
that past Monday was the cover-up uncovered, the smoking-gun
tape, as they were calling it, revealed. Nixon had known all along,
which no one doubted. And now, a change of presidency would
be marked by my emergence, by my being unveiled, revealed. I
would come out glistening with hope and possibility, a national-
reconciliation baby, a heal-the-wounds baby, a time-to-move-on
baby.

She sits there through the slowly increasing frequency of contractions and watches Nixon standing, now, on the top step of the
presidential helicopter, his arms spread wide, making his trade-
mark V with each hand, amazed that if you didn't know better
you'd say this was a man declaring victory before adoring multi-
tudes, that this was a triumphal sendoff. The phrase *Peace with
honor* rumbles through her head, a phrase which disguised the
fact of defeat with further killing. She thinks with pleasure of how
badly her father will be taking this, her father who identifies with
all expressions of authority and obeisance toward it. *Peace with
honor.* The hypocrisy of honor. And she vows then and there that
there will be respect shown in her household but no honor.
Respect will be honored, not honor respected, she will insist on
that. She is surprised how strongly she feels about it, about everything, really. She will have to live what she believes and not simply
believe it.

She watches the swearing in of Gerald Ford, the thirty-eighth president of the United States, one hand on a black book, the other uplifted, repeating the oath of office after the Chief Justice of the Supreme Court. Something about hearing the oath said twice, like a marriage vow, made it so moving to her, a ritual in which the said and the done felt as close together as something repeated word for word.

Now the big, black helicopter with the former president in it lifts, weightless as a fish in the sea, tilts, swings around, veers off and up, off-camera; she shakes off the trance of Big Events and makes her calls again, the phone a black, Bakelite rotary thing, whose holes her forefinger hooks in and whips round and round, the dial winding and unwinding, ziiip, click, click, click, click, click, ziiip, click, click, click: no answer, no answer, busy, busy, busy; the contractions are not just closer together, they are coming harder, stronger.

Don't I know it.

Gingerly, she takes herself to the hospital, as if she is carrying inside her a very large and fragile egg.

My father finds the note, taped to a cold can of Rheingold, his first stop when he gets home. At the hospital, he walks beside her in the obstetrics waiting area. She can't sit, or sit still. She has already been there for hours, the small suitcase beside her. A doctor has examined her and found her to be only two centimeters dilated. But it's early yet. The hospital crowded. Frank, my inseminarian, is nervous, attentive. He goes out to smoke now and again and brings her back some gum to chew, Hostess cupcakes, too, which he eats. Her throat is dry, but she isn't hungry. Though the contractions keep coming, every seven minutes or so, nothing is happening.

If you ask me, a lot is happening. But no one asks the hammer. Or the point of the punch. The witness. The Deep Throat. Here I am, at the center of the action, the smoking gun, an umbilical cord around my neck like a feather boa. I've got the tapes. But no one bothers to ask me. So what do they get? Disinformation. Formerly known as misinformation, as in:

At midnight, Frank is told to go home, it will be a while yet but they have to keep her here, under observation, she'll be in good hands. Not to worry, they'll make her comfortable. They place her on a gurney, which is worse to her than sitting or standing, but they insist; they give her something for the pain. A nurse pats her hand, and she is forgotten even before the nurse turns away. She lies there alone. Not alone. She has me. From now on, it's the two of us. But, for both of us, for now, it doesn't feel that way.

It's not a hug anymore. Nor am I being called. I am not being warmly greeted at the start of a brilliant career. I am not being ushered, convoyed, shepherded, bullied into open air, into the Outside. The age of tenderness is over. The age of solicitude, of gentle nudging and encouragement, is through. Loyal support, the fellowship of team play, participatory democracy, consensus building. Done with. Nor is it every man for himself, either. It's a little like getting a corner man's shoulder massage in the ring before the opening bell. A little like being a bobsled rocked back and forth before the four-man team sprints off. A little like. And then it's more like being a bullet driven into the chamber. But that's not even quite it. The squeezing is now directional. Less hug, more push. Way less. It has become purposeful, single-minded. And I'm not a toboggan or a bullet, it's not a gun: the entire maternal biologic contraption resembles nothing so much as a siege engine. A siege engine in reverse. Under siege, the walled town has prospered and grown. It has received support, advisors, weaponry, foreign troops, a vast influx of cash, supplies, corporate involvement. And now, the time has come to bust down the doors. The siege engine is a battering ram whose job is to break not out but in, except in this case. And I am the ramming agent itself, the simple technology, my head slammed up against the cervix with each contracting rush. Then I am drawn backward, as though by the effort of many trembling arms and heaved forward to shiver and splinter the massive doors. We have not been prepared for this. We have not been told what this was really like. *A just peace,* we were told. *Vietnamization. Pacification.* But no. That was the talk. Carpet-bombing, it was. Defoliation. The space between the verbal and material realities is large enough to drive a scream through. We are passing the fail-safe point. No cease-fire. No truce. No peace talks. No articles of surrender, no resignations accepted. No negotiated settlement. That was all talk. This is the real thing. It has taken over. Operation Rolling Thunder.

There is no calling us back. Yet she calls, calls out. She hollers.

Nurses hold her hand. Hold up her head and give her drinks of water and are gone. I am being swung into the taut unyielding doors. She cries out with each ram. As I would, too, if I could cry out. She is the doors. And on the other side? No one. Who is besieged if not her? Who is the besieger if not I? And yet I am trying to get out, not in. There are the doors which must be gotten through. "Doors" is just a figure of speech. A sphincterish knothole. Just another figure. Window, partially open. Another figure. Flesh of my flesh? What isn't a way of talking? On the other side of it, nothing. Nothing I could see could I put my eye to the unplugged opening. Nothing but the world. For which there are only words. To enter it, I put my head down and push, am pushed.

She is left there parked against the wall, the wheels locked, through the night. An orderly mops the halls. Another steers a cleaning dolly in behind her, leaves it there with its scalpel-smell of antiseptic. Two nurses go by. "Well, I don't see what's so illegitimate about it. So what that they're both not elected? I mean, it's not like I elected my boyfriend. I just kind of picked him. He was cute, and his family has money. Same thing with Nelson Rockefeller, right? Although, between you and me, I don't see my Dominic lasting out his term of office." They titter. It's as if she is not there. The belief that came over her earlier has shown itself to be illusory. Not only is she not even history writ small, she is so small and insignificant, she wonders as the nurses pass if she is really there at all.

A doctor examines her once. Three centimeters dilated. Meaning not much, although he holds his thumb and forefinger up the way someone makes the "This close!" gesture. Just relax, he tells her. Relax, you're doing fine. But she doesn't feel fine. Neither do I. Later, after dawn, she is hurried into the surgical theater. Lots of hectic behavior, rushing around. In her delirium, though, as she is put under the anesthetic, it reminds her of a press conference, reporters and photographers crowding round, jostling to get in closer, flashbulbs going off, microphones being pushed toward her mouth. Such a sudden and intrusive interest. A moment ago it was as if she didn't exist. Now they are hanging on her every word. As it should be. Nothing will be the same after this. Not through legislation, backroom horse-trading or executive order, but she is, nevertheless, changing lives, hers and Frank's; she will take her rightful place in the family, to her sister's chagrin, motherhood will accomplish that. And she will have brought me into the world, the crowning deed. It may be going on every day, but the act of creation is no small feat. All praise be due. A silence has fallen over the multitude. They are waiting expectantly. The cameras are running. She surveys their faces from the podium, she takes in the pulsating greenness of the grass, the rose garden beyond, the velvety petals in the sunlight like a shadowed red. She hasn't prepared a statement, yet she has so much she wants to say about matters large and small. I am, she begins.

I am, too, I chime in. Me, too. I pound my bald, battered head against the knocker, the keyhole, the coffered panels of the great bronze doors which have begun to open outward, widen like the eye's iris. The top of my head is cool, a sensation I have never known. And then it's like pulling on a hat that's too tight. I am ready with my speech. Before all else, I want to say, I am. Neither more nor less. The last and latest, the first, the ur- and only. I am because I am. You shall have no other gods before thee is another way of putting it.

The first cry is the story of clambering out. It is the story of space-capsule endurance, of its triumph and exhaustion, its tenacity fused with a farewelling sorrow. Its epic, wailing rhythm can only mirror, like the big bang's background radiation, the uterine convulsions—breathing itself the accordion approximation of expulsion. What isn't about *in* and *out*, like the systole-diastole of the heart, hers and mine, paired for so long and, suddenly now, solo—I am emergent, on the verge of my first performance, preparing that cry which is meant to be the totality of what I am, the first thing I shall make, a sound, music only to my ears, perhaps, which distills everything I know and want into a single, stark expression. She hears it, too, in her sedation, hears it in anticipation, knowing what it will sound like because it will, ventriloquist that I am, speak for her, too. Perhaps it will be all the more perfect and true for not coming out, after all, the cord crimped and squeezing as I stall in the crowning position, choking me before I know what choking is, and I am going blue, they cannot see it yet, though even my blueness is beautiful.

I am he who would have loved the sunlight and eyelight, incandescent light and starlight and tree light and all manner of shine and flick and fluttering, moth and flag and leaf. I am he who would have savored the sweetness of human milk, the satisfaction of suck and glut, mouthings of every size and shape, of the very smell pouring from the skin. I would have been pure body, all squirm and grasp and seize and pull closer. The ear a mouth, the mouth an eye, the eye a way of laying hands on. The mobile of cows and ducks and pigs rooting in the air above the empty crib would have affirmed my cry, called it unimpeachable, true, would have bleated and mooed and quacked back. My cry the fury and ecstasy and contentment and joyousness of *yes!* wrapped around a germinating kernel of *no*. This is the cry she'll remember hearing, which, to my own surprise, I will not make. And, it's true, I was made to sing, this sound and my life twinned. It may be I am too proud to speak, the song I am to sing may be too precious to me to let out, to share, though the intent and urge to sing is great. I will always be haunted, by whether it was my choice to make.

When she comes out of sedation, she hears the after-echoes of my cry the way one continues to hear a siren in the silence after it stops. The doctor comes in. She looks to him in expectation. *My baby?* she says. *Where's my baby? Is it a boy or a girl?*

A boy, he replies, and as she begins to smile as no one has seen her smile since. He adds, quickly, *It was a boy. Your son was stillborn, I'm so sorry to have to say.*

No, she says quietly, in disagreement, like the telltale buffet of wind before the storm. *I'm sorry,* the young doctor says again, *we could not revive him. Even if we had,* he goes on, *it's likely he would have suffered irreversible brain damage.* Then, gathering, it comes, the squall, still slowed by disbelief, *No!* she shrieks. *NO! I want to see my son! Bring me my son!* My dad, Y-chromosome dispenser, already reconciled not to be my dad, obedient as a soldier, rushes in along with Madeleine's sister and mother. *Where is he?!* my mother is shouting. *Where is he?!*

Calm down, honey, lie down, darling, they implore. *You'll tear yourself up.* They try to keep her from getting to her feet. *No!* she howls. *Let me go! I want to see my baby!* She screams and slaps at them.

But already she can't hear my voice over the din of her own and theirs. My tinny a cappella can only be heard in silence, its soaring sound like a cicada's wherever silence like grass grows thick and high. In the cacophony, the song of me departed, although I can still hear it like a dream of paradise.

*

Afterwards, the fish sang a different tune. Afterwards, the four and twenty blackbirds baked in the pie blackened and charred and never sang again. The eensy weensy spider never clambered up the waterspout a second time. The black sheep, baa-baa, gave to master and dame far more than its three bags full. The shine was off the apple. And the apple lay deliquescing under the tree, not far from it but sour, windblown, visited by bug and bear. The fish now told her a different tale altogether.

Only a month later she sat in this same spot on a Sunday morning in September, a spot she could be found sitting at any and all hours, removed from history both public and personal, stroking her belly, or rather, stroking the air where her belly and I inside it, like a carnival that has folded its rides and struck its tents, had been. When the new president appeared on the screen and announced to the American people in his earnest, weight-of-the-world-on-his-shoulders voice that "It could go on and on and on, or someone must write the end to it. I have concluded that only I can do that, and if I can, I must," she slid to the rough, plaid edge of her seat and shouted "No!" at the screen, at him. She felt coming what she hadn't sensed coming before. She did not believe in the end of anything anymore, nor in beginnings, she wanted things to go and on, and she hated that it was so, but she wanted nothing to change, because change was for the worse, it was her way of holding on, and when the president went on to say he was granting Richard Nixon "a full, free, and absolute pardon," she shrieked it again, "No!" that wildest word in the English language, and snapped off the tube. If all hope was to be incinerated, no one should be let off the hook, no one.

(And I feel that "No!" as a shudder through my dorsal fin since I'd become a dolphin kicking toward the warm waters of the Gulf Stream, free of disappointment and the treason of attachment, weightless, carving effortlessly through the largest of wombs, whose watery world will not break: she sent her great negation out, and the hook at the end of that "No!" snagged my jaw, the line went taut, sinking the hook deeper, the barb set itself, and I was caught, as you shall see, reeled back in, returned to my jealous and vigilant origins.)

"Sweetheart, it was an awful thing to lose the baby," the depatered familias would say, having forgotten me, already looking ahead to the next bright thing, "but you can't go around all the time like an egg with its chicken cut off." This when the first flakes of snow had begun to fall, early, that autumn. To my madonna, they fell like blackbirds, frosted-over. She saw them falling out of the sky, a migratory gathering of them going dead in the midst of their great wheeling confab, blackening the already cloud-smudged sky. Invisible to others, they landed all about her, so that she had to wade through them, lifting them up, looking for signs of life. They melted away in her hands as she listened for a heart-beat, a black yet still blinking eye amid the carnage of beak and wing and claw.

"Jeez," the august pants of our unfamily implored, "like an egg with its head cut off you are. You've got to get a grip on yourself, sweetheart. It's a sad thing, but the truth is, it's not the end of the world. We still have each other, don't we?"

But all she heard was a maelstrom of torn wings as my sonless father comforted her not with apples but with a renewal of affection, that is, with sex, to which she submitted, if not exactly succumbed—a prolonged though tender hydraulic event that she experienced as a piling up of birds on her heart. She knew the truth was entirely other than one of growth and hope; the future was something that was traded like potatoes and sow bellies in the pit of the commodities exchange; she knew the market, *en point*, turned on misfortune; she knew, now, the true, fishy truth.

Goldie and Locks now spoke to her of this world of otherwise, and she no longer rubbed the sides of her shriveled tummy, which when she'd done it in those last weeks had begun inexplicably to feel like wheels going backwards, as though someone had climbed out of his truck without setting the hand break. Hardly gathering speed at first, I was, nevertheless, rolling back down a hill to wreck at the bottom, where all the possibilities lay expiring in a heap like fish out of water. Yet the motion of her hands had lulled me even as I was about to slide away; they seemed to be waving in welcome, in greeting: hello, traveler, we salute you at the outset of a glorious career! Well, every misunderstanding is a valediction.

She could hardly see the fish now as she knelt in front of their bowl with her hands limp in her lap, unflopping. The bowl was soupy with algae, and the algae was a yellowish-green and thick. The bubbler wheezed phlegmatically, the filter clogged. The fish wriggled without getting anywhere as if crawling along hard ground on their bellies, and their mouth places yawned open with greater effort each day. Like flags snapping too long in the wind and sun, they were faded and shredding. Sometimes she remembered to feed them. Even when she couldn't see them floating through the branching murk, she sat and listened to them as the radiators hissed and clanged, steaming the windows, beyond which birds were plunging, splattering down, out of their element.

"Jeez, darling, let it go," begged the increasingly erstwhile love of that part of her life, husband number one and only, who sold refrigerators at the time and knew everything there was to know about coolants and compression ratios and crispers, "you're no different than a chicken with its egg cut off." By now she used the perambulator to bring things back to their apartment.

First it was dead birds which she packed in the freezer. Then a crow with a broken wing. She led home gaunt mangy curs and fed them raw lamb chops. A litter of kittens whose sharp tiny mouths she spooned mashed potatoes into. She brought home baffled old men who'd lost their way to the smoke shop and sat them in front of the fish tank as though it were a TV. She'd wrap their gnarled hands around a mug of creamed corn.

"Jeez, honey, you're taking things a bit far, don't you think? It's like the SPCA and the Port Authority all rolled up into one around here. What are you, Florence Nightingale or something? You're running around like a chicken with its head cut off. I'm tired of the same lamb chop night after night. Don't I have some rights around here, too? Enough's enough, for Christ's sake. Look, it tears me up, too. But you don't see me mooning over it. It's time you started doing something. You could be a teacher's aide or a nurse's aide like your friend Ethel. What do you say we drive this old codger home—haven't I seen him here before? What does he do, get lost like clockwork? Then we'll go out to dinner. I don't know about you, but I could use a change. Come on." This from the nominal head of our enucleated unit.

That night she gazed into his adoring, present-tense eyes as he raised a glass of wine to she-couldn't-hear-what, and she watched birds spiraling down like MIGs through his gray-blue irises to crash and burn in the black flames of his pupils. "To us," he toasted. "To the future. We deserve a little happiness, too, don't you think?"

The fish, in whose presence the old men she brought home often remembered their errands or the street where they lived, began to give up the big picture for details. *You won't find him here,* they writhed. *Little boy lost, go blow your horn. Sheep's in the meadow, the cow's in the corn. Go. Go.* As they sank lower and lower in the tank, flickering in spastic circles on their sides, they began pointing like compass needles. She would set out in the mornings, as though going to work herself, and stop women with baby carriages to ooh or ahh, to follow at a distance.

She haunted the laundromats, warm and soap-scented, noisy with productive agitation. She'd wheel in all the items in the layette she had picked out with her mother, the little T-shirts and pullovers, the sheets and socks, the burping towels and footed pajamas that looked like snowsuits with their busy Bambi or alphabet patterns. She'd wash them and read magazines, dry and fold the unworn pile, observing the coughing, lollipop-sucking children led in by their mothers. And she'd smile a fixed rictus of a smile at the toddlers who staggered past or stopped with wobbly stare to steady themselves on her legs, their strong fists clutching.

The fish pointed her to the schoolyard where the K-through-5 kids would emerge for recess. They poured from the doors and down the metal steps. Without pause or ceremony they began kicking balls against the brick-red wall, pumped swings up to dizzying heights, bounced the seesaws hard into the macadam, bucking their partners high off the yellow-painted planks. Everything seemed to be going up, up. Even their voices went high with excitement and shot up and away, pulling their bodies along like Apollo 11 taking off and rocketing into outer space, no thought of coming back. That's what they were after. Kids. They wanted purely to be the thing that muscled its way up, they wanted to kick that rubber ball like a howitzer right through the walls of their school and bring the whole immovable edifice down. If that's not joy incarnate, I don't know what is.

She watched them swing from and climb frantically through the bars of the jungle gym pursued by whoever was "it." Tag: such an odd game if you thought about it. It gave power to the oddball, the outcast, the freak. In the end no one could protect herself or fight back or gang up. If you were "it," no one stood up to you; everyone ran. Now you were special, possessed of powers, contagious. It conferred status. Everybody wanted to be "it," alone and the center of attention all at once.

They ran, shrieked, pushed, hit, hurt, all of them, in turn, "it," and they washed over her, waves and photons of them, impulsive, chaotic, and happy even to her whose eyes roamed that kaleidoscope of elementary motions for the one, the needle-in-this-haystack who was not any different, but who nevertheless didn't belong, because, although he couldn't know it, he belonged to her. And she'd know who he was because she'd sense in him a weak "it," a wounded, ill-at-ease being, sucking the thumb of his own weak existence, someone they'd tease and call a baby or mama's boy, who didn't fight back or know how to.

The fish had said, "Look," or "Looook," liplessly stretching their mouths forward as if sucking at a spoonful of hot broth; that drawn out *oo* sound made it clear to her she would have to search high and low. She trailed her cold hand over the chain links as she moved along the schoolyard fence, observing the rhythms of hopscotch and jump rope, scanning the red cheeks, the earmuffs, the runny noses. Until through the fence, her fingertips snagged on hair, a head. A boy. Balled up. In a brown wool coat he had retracted his face and hands into. Like a turtle. A girl, an older girl with red knee-high socks and saddle shoes, was turning from him and saying, "Be that way."

"Hey," she said, squatting down close behind him, like a toad. They were the only two reptiles in sight. All the rest were children. They, the only amphibians, but more likely fish out of water.

"Hey," she said. "You're a turtle, aren't you? I'm a frog. Brribit! What sort of sound do you make?" The boy didn't move, his face buried in his collar. Six, maybe seven, he was small for his age.

"Hey," she said. "Know where we can get some good insects to eat?"

"Brribit!" she repeated. She leaned forward until she was against the fence, too. She could feel his thin spine against her leg.

"Brribit!" she said again, beside his ear.

"Turtles don't say brribit," came a sound, muffled, from inside the coat. "Turtles say tuurrtlllle! That's why they're turtles. Don't you know anything?"

"Oh," she replied. "I must be a brribit! then and not a frog."

"Frogs say bribit. Only turtles say tuurrtle. Everybody knows a frog doesn't say froggg. Boy, are you dumb. You must be dumb as a stump." One eye emerged from the collar and eyed her mistrustfully.

"Well, you're right. That's because I am a stump. Do you know what a stump says?"

"Stumps don't say anything."

"They most certainly do," she answered. She could see the girl who had walked away talking with a matronly woman on duty by the stairs. It was always women like this, humorless types, built like fire hydrants. Graying hair cut close to her head like a helmet. "Just because it has no branches or leaves anymore doesn't mean a stump can't speak."

"Yeah? So what do they say?" he asked, his second eye coming up and opening. Just like a crocodile. Now the girl was pointing in their direction.

"Do you like goldfish?" she asked him. It wasn't far to the gate in the fence, which was closed but not padlocked.

"What's that got to do with stumps?"

"My goldfish are lonely. They come right up to the glass with their big eyes looking for a friend." The woman was now making her way over, the girl following in her wake. Swarming children parted like the sea to let her through yet without seeming to pay her any mind.

"I bet my fish would like to meet a turtle," she cajoled.

"Is this your child, ma'am?" the lady asked.

"Yes." She got up. "He's my turtle."

"Do you know this lady, Stuart?" the woman said to the boy. Voice like a band saw.

"Uh-huh. She's a stump." Good for him, asserting himself like that, she thought. What drew women like this to look after children? Unsmiling, they were stolid, impervious to anything but order. She knew what maternal was.

"She's a what?" this unmotherly woman barked.

"A stump," the boy repeated, uncurling himself, turning to my mother.

"What's a stump say?" he asked, accusingly, as if she'd taken something of his.

She was already beginning to walk away, but she turned and tried to say his name. She couldn't. Stuart. She would never call a child Stuart. Standing there hostile, sullen, half-interested in spite of himself. He'd lost his "it," she realized, because he was prematurely aged. His crabbed name didn't help. Stuart. He'd be smart, but spiteful. He was a Stuart through and through, she could see that now that he was standing up; he was probably just waiting for the day he would be in charge of something. Make the rules. Exclude others. Say, *No, you can't, that won't be possible, we can't allow it.* He'd say it without the least regret or the appearance of regret. Fragile now, he'd be all about getting even later, inflicting harm. No, this was not her child. She looked at him. Already an old man.

"A stump," she called out to him, "says dumb. It says dumb, dumb, dumb, dumb, dumb." And then she was running. Still, she felt she could have saved him, even a kid like that. But she knew that this one wasn't hers. Anyone could see that. She began to mistrust the fish.

But one fish took to floating on the surface and pointing magnetically in a new direction with its unmoving eye. She followed its needle back to the hospital where her life had blossomed and ended. She stood outside the glassed-in baby room of the maternity ward; it felt to her like a giant fish tank, the rows of newbies swaddled in white cotton in that bright white room, a pink or blue ribbon attached to each. Silky black heads stuck out of cotton blankets, each an apoplectic or swarthy color the exact shade, she couldn't get it out of her mind, of my un-Pop's genitals. She'd lean with her forehead to the glass beside doting mothers in hospital gowns, fathers looking awkward yet beaming, grandfolks tapping the glass, cooing. Sometimes they'd ask which infant was hers, and she'd point to a baby furthest away; they would tell her it was darling, congratulations, you must be so happy, and in return they would ask, Isn't our grandson, our niece, our godchild, whoever, beautiful, a bruiser, a regular Caruso? The nurses who moved among the stainless-steel baskets rewrapping, giving them bottles, reminded her of worker bees crawling over the capped brood cells in the hive. This was where the hive replenished itself. Where the cells divided, where tissue differentiated. It smelled like honey to her, cloying, too much. And yet, somehow she knew this wasn't the place. But she could feel herself getting close, getting closer.

When the second fish floated up to join the first and turn like the two hands of a wind-up clock, they sent her back to the hospital; she found the small room where the preemies were housed; like smacked spiders they lay on their backs, naked but for a diaper in heated glass Quonset cases. Three of them. They were so tiny, so wrinkled and thin. Their shriveled fingers, the volutes of their ears, their nostrils, were so precise, so detailed, so miniature. Such wizened little people. A family of little people. As if they'd lived their entire life *in utero* and had emerged from the birth canal as old men and women, already nearing their end. One was clearly her child. The one in the middle. The smallest of the three. The one, head square as a wall safe, who resembled her father. The diaper pins, the size of the infant's foot, filled her with pity. So delicate. So beautiful. So helpless. So clearly hers. Even the nurses couldn't help but noticing.

And when the policeman who answered the hospital's call coaxed her home in the squad car, walked her up the stairs, saw her into the apartment, tipped his brim to her when she said, *Thank you, I am fine now, officer,* and left, she carried the fetid bowl of water into the bathroom, poured the no-longer-talking fish down the toilet, and threw the bowl out the window, where it shattered on the sidewalk just as the cop car pulled away. The exploding slivers of glass glinted up into the air like so many small white birds.

"Dear Frank," began the note. It was a brief scrawl whose gist was (although my dam was never anything but obliquely angled): this chicken's taking her head and her eggs with her. And when she finished it she wrapped it around a bottle of Pabst Blue Ribbon he was sure to reach for; she packed a suitcase larger than the one she'd readied for her hospital stay, left the door half-open for a clue, and went out, where didn't matter to her, for good.

This was after the troops had come home, as Saigon was falling to the Viet Cong, the NVA. That, too, was the utter end. You could see the footage of gunships weighted with human cargo lifting like carpenter bees, slowly, almost too heavy to rise, from the American Embassy roof. Vietnamese whose fortunes were tied to the departing Americans and who feared to stay behind were clinging to the landing skids, swaying from ropes or rope ladders. She was getting away. Going down the stairs, she could hear the blades of the chopper going whompwhompwhomp-whomp, and she could feel herself spiraling up slowly above these rooftops into the sky where no matter your destination you couldn't hold on for long.

A Profile by Dan Chiasson

As the work of Rosanna Warren reminds us, to be a poet is to be a writer of poems. The forces of abstraction that threaten always to turn real individual artworks into mere manifestations of moods or (worse) theories or (worst of all) institutions—these forces go limp before poems so brilliantly made. The sculptures are not here to show the museum to advantage. Warren's poems are original in that they differ from other people's poems, but also because, beautifully, they differ from one another. Having a "style" for so many artists is like having a chronic condition whose symptoms crop up predictably, season to season, year to year. For Warren, having a style means having a kind of kit for making surprises.

That kit includes some fine tools, some of which had to have been shaped during Warren's remarkable childhood. To be the daughter of a pair of celebrated writers (Robert Penn Warren and Eleanor Clark), who were also present and loving parents, would seem a rare bit of luck. Warren was born in Fairfield, Connecticut, in 1953. Like Humbert Humbert, her earliest memory of rapture involved Poe's "Annabel Lee," which she found on the shelves of her parents' fire-lit library one evening after being given, by parents of a friend, "a half glass of wine at dinner." This story, both a myth of consecration (the fire, the wine) and, very lightly, a parody of such myths, evinces the intelligence and resourcefulness—and the playfulness—that marks Warren's work. Another story from her childhood has her wheeling John Crowe Ransom (a "regal benignity") around in her doll's perambulator. Her childhood sometimes appears like a peaceable kingdom of weirdly docile geniuses, with a child in charge.

Of course, as any writer knows, writing thrives on adverse conditions. Because Warren's writing has thrived so beautifully, it is tempting to think that the conditions of her childhood must have been, at least in part, adverse. It cannot have been easy to make a life as a writer with her parents' successes at her back. The difficulty of writing poems that approach the power of the work one loves: this difficulty is apt to seem more formidable, not less, if a person has had Ransom in her perambulator. Her parents and their friends grew to become writers, she says, "by reading and by hanging out with other writers"—not, that is, by hanging out with their parents. Becoming a writer feels (it felt to me, at least) much more like saying "No" than saying "Yes": how is it a writer says "no" to a childhood like Warren's? For she did manifestly become a writer; she has published four books of poems (*Snow Day, Each Leaf Shines Separate, Stained Glass,* which won the Lamont Poetry Prize, and *Departure*), and was a chancellor of the Academy of American Poets (her term ended in 2005). How *did* a person like Warren become a writer?

First, by becoming a painter. "As a child I didn't draw a great distinction between writing and painting. Both involved the hand," she says, "and translating seeing into some sort of form." Spoken, one might say, like a writer; but spoken, also, like a writer whose first art she never entirely abandoned, and whose principles still inform—deeply, as both subject and technique—her poems. Her counter-life as a painter is suggested by her brilliant visual inventiveness. (The New England stubble fields from an airplane window are a "dun, scuffed, moulting carpet" while a lover's presence is at once "an image upon shaken waters" and "the muscled slide of waters in mid / stroke.") But it seems especially suggestive that, though Warren was "always a figurative painter," nevertheless she says she worked on "the strangeness of the world." This tension between opposing intuitions (the world can be depicted with clarity; the world is strange and, therefore, always a little ahead of or apart from its depictions) is a fundamental principle of Warren's poems.

Translating ancient poems—particularly Ancient Greek and Latin—has also given her what it gives many poets: a feeling for literary beauty as it inheres in "the fabric" of poems—in syntax, in idiom, in versification. Perhaps no poet of Warren's eminence now knows the Classics so well at such close range. But just as forensics don't add up to life, metrics don't make a poem. The spirit behind Warren's Classical scholarship, it seems to me, is the pursuit of vivid estrangement from what she has called "our little selfhoods." The faint silliness of being a person, of clinging to

Mike Minehan

episodes and atmospheres so central to oneself, while to the world so tangential and evaporative—is this a comic or a tragic point? True that art can make anything permanent. If a blush can have engendered Wyatt's "My Galley Charged with Forgetfulness" or a glance given us Sappho's "Phainetai Moi," had we better hoard our blushes and our glances? The Classics have helped Warren articulate both the contingent nature of selves in time (bound by whatever conventions of speech and thought obtained at a given moment) and the permanence of art as a way out of selfhood, a way to transform the small souvenirs and trinkets of its existence in history. As she writes in a poem called "Portrait: Marriage": "now is a proposition / molded over and over / in water, loam and stone."

Warren has worked a range of complex operations on foreign texts, from the most "faithful" translation (notably of Euripides) to the loosest riff. To find oneself already represented in texts, texts long circulating in the cultural bloodstream, and yet to be the only witness to the discovery: this Borgesian or Rimbaudian problem is explored in a sequence of poems called "From the Notebooks of Anne Verveine," which is included in her collection *Departure*. The poems are faux-found and "translated" works of a made-up French poet a generation Warren's junior. These are erotic poems, emphatically and conventionally so, finding a pitch that Warren's work otherwise seems nearly to repudiate ("Some Gallic reach of mind," Warren has said, was needed to circumvent her "New England censoring mechanisms.") It is important that the most "naked" poems she has done (though everywhere the conventions that indicate "nakedness" obtain) rest on this mountain of complex thinking and counter-thinking about poetry. Part of the pleasure of her Anne Verveine poems comes from hearing a poignant voice express itself in artless terms; subsequent, even deeper pleasures, await the reader who thinks carefully about questions like the following: What counts as "artless" in works of art? How and why do poets present their own poems as "original" as distinct from translation, collage, and pastiche? You cannot not consider these issues when you read these poems; but in doing so you are reconstituting in your own mind the forces of culture and discourse that threaten to muffle, under their heft, the little heartbroken voices that make lyric poetry so riveting. What is a reader to do?

When it all comes together for Warren, as in the Anne Verveine poems or in the short elegy for her mother called "Simile," there seems simply more for readers *to do* with Warren's work than with the work of even her finest contemporaries. "Simile" is a poem about how a person one loves looks when harrowed, when agonized. Warren's mother is sitting upright in a hospital bed, her hands gripping the metal rails. She is frightened, and, as we know from the poem, she is near dying. Here is the extended Homeric simile that opens the poem:

> As when her friend, the crack Austrian skier, in the story
> she often told us, had to face
> his first Olympic ski jump and, from
> the starting ramp over the chute that plunged
> so vertiginously its bottom lip
> disappeared from view, gazed
> on the horizon of Alps that swam and dandled around him
> like toy boats in a bathtub, and he could not
> for all his iron determination,
> training and courage
> ungrip his fingers from the railings of the starting gate,
> so that

his teammates had to join in prying
up, finger by finger, his hands
to free him, so

The poem continues after a stanza break that feels like an indrawn breath: "facing death, my / mother gripped the bedrails..." "As" and "so" are the end terms that bracket a simile that includes a sub-simile ("like toy boats"), suggesting that what one does when facing oblivion (the tragic oblivion of death or the comic oblivion of a steep Alpine run) is to find recourse in figurative language. The figuration fails, finally: the mother is not a skier, even a "crack" skier; those mountain peaks are not toy boats. Reality—vertiginous, immediate—will prevail, and (as the mother must once have told her children) the only thing for a person to do is to face it head-on. The poem's single headlong sentence leaps the stanza break, like a fugitive chased across rooftops, leaping while fleeing, until it ends where the life ends: with the loosening of hands.

Poems are great to the degree that they overcome a skeptical reader's permanent resistance to being powerfully moved. I am almost never moved; I am deeply moved by "Simile." That is one way you know a poem is great. But "Simile" is great in an additional and very unusual way: it helps us think more deeply and more precisely about poetry, its claim upon the world, its claim upon its readers. How a poem can fulfill both functions, breaking one's heart even as it makes one think, is a secret that only a handful of living poets know at any one time. Rosanna Warren seems to me now among that small group of secret-sharers.

POSTSCRIPTS

ZACHARIS AWARD *Ploughshares* is pleased to present Thomas Sayers Ellis with the sixteenth annual John C. Zacharis First Book Award for his collection of poems, *The Maverick Room* (Graywolf, 2005). The $1,500 award, which is named after Emerson College's former president, honors the best debut book by a *Ploughshares* writer, alternating annually between poetry and fiction.

This year's judge was the poet John Skoyles, who is a *Ploughshares* trustee. In choosing the collection, Skoyles said: "In *The Maverick Room*, Thomas Sayers Ellis jostles sound and sense and comes up with a new and winning combination of both. These poems sing and whisper, shout and confide, in the same unmistakable voice. Lyric and narrative strains fuse in poem after poem, making the collection as far-reaching as it is profound."

Thomas Sayers Ellis's recent publications include *Poetry, Tin House, Legitimate Dangers: American Poets of the New Century, Zoland Poetry,* and *Under the Rock Umbrella: Contemporary Poets from 1951–1977.* He has received a Whiting Writer's Award and fellowships from the Fine Arts Work Center in Provincetown, the MacDowell Colony, Yaddo, and the Bread Loaf Writers' Conference. He has published two chapbooks, *The Good Junk* in 1996, which was included in the *Agni*/Graywolf series *Take Three,* and *The Genuine Negro Hero* in 2001, from Kent State University, and a chaplet, *Song On,* in 2005, from WinteRed Press. He has also co-edited the anthology *On the Verge: Emerging Poets and Artists* (Faber & Faber) and edited the forthcoming *Quotes Community: Notes for Black Poets* (Michigan).

Ellis was born in 1963 in Washington, D.C., where his mother was a swing manager at McDonald's and his father worked for the city reading water meters. Ellis's two great childhood ambitions were to draw and to be a football player, "specifically a great halfback," he says, "a runner, like Gale Sayers, who I was named after, because of my speed, which should explain my prosody." At Paul Laurence Dunbar High School, he didn't play football, but was a swimmer, the editor of the school newspaper, and the president of the creative writing club. He also played the timbales and other percussion instruments for local go-go bands.

For several years, Ellis attended Harvard, but never received his degree. "I was a passionate student who could only commit to the subjects I was interested in: literature and cinema." He received quite an education in those two fields, studying with Seamus Heaney, serving as a teaching assistant for Spike Lee, and working as a projectionist at the Harvard Film Archive. He also worked at two bookstores, the Grolier Poetry Book Shop and Trident Booksellers, and while living in Cambridge co-founded The Dark Room Collective, a network of African-American poets that  included Sharan Strange, Kevin Young, Natasha Trethewey, John Keene, Tracy K. Smith, and Major Jackson. The Collective became famous for its lively, standing-room-only readings, which mixed emerging writers with established poets, backed by jazz performances; it was the sole reading series in the Boston area devoted to writers of color. After Cambridge, Ellis went to Brown University and studied with Michael S. Harper, receiving his M.F.A. in 1995—"the two quickest years of my life," he says.

His first publications were in *Agni* and *Callaloo*, pretty much simultaneously, a day or two apart. "I met the editors of both of these journals in places where I should not have been," Ellis recalls, "so I would advise young writers not to try to control and calculate their paths too much, to shoot for a balance of accident and aim." His other early publications were in *The Kenyon Review* and *Grand Street*, and then in *APR*, *The Pushcart Prize*, and twice in *The Best American Poetry*.

"I am influenced by everything I come in contact with," Ellis says, "and most of my work is about not making distinctions, of eliminating false boundaries. My major influences are noises and gesture and other pre-language behaviors. *The Maverick Room* is an attempt to order the chaos and chaos the order of my relationships to Washington, D.C., and poetry. I wanted to create the beginnings of a percussive prosody that was governed by more than literary intelligence and logical lyrical progression sprinkled with similes. I wanted to begin the process of being courageous and honest enough to commit to a risk in every room. And, well, like the speaker from 'Hush Yo Mouf,' I failed."

Formerly an associate professor at Case Western Reserve University, Ellis is now teaching at Sarah Lawrence College and in Lesley University's low-residency M.F.A. program. He lives in New York City and is working on a new manuscript, *Colored Only: Identity Repair Poems.*

VOLUNTEERS AND TRUSTEES We would like to thank our volunteer readers and interns, who are listed on the second page of the masthead, for their generous efforts. Our thanks, too, to our trustees for their support: Marillyn Zacharis, Jacqueline Liebergott, DeWitt Henry, Helene Atwan, William H. Berman, Robert E. Courtemanche, Tim Huggins, Elaine Markson, Grafton Nunes, Janet Silver, and John Skoyles.

SUBSCRIBERS Please note that on occasion we exchange mailing lists with other literary magazines and organizations. If you would like your name excluded from these exchanges, simply send us a letter or e-mail message stating so. Our e-mail address is pshares@emerson.edu. Also, please inform us of any address changes with as much advance notice as possible. The post office usually will not forward bulk mail.

*Books Recommended by
Our Staff Editors*

Mosquito, *poems by Alex Lemon* (Tin House): The poems in Alex Lemon's striking first book document the experience of undergoing brain surgery, an agonizing recovery, and the sudden discovery of Eros, who finally emerges as the ultimate emblem of survival. Careful yet raw, the fresh sutures that comprise the lines in many of these poems sing of pain so sharply as to verge on ethereal. Yet, in other poems, Lemon approaches recollection as a butcher does a carcass, bludgeoning necessarily harsh and decisive strikes in order to determine the boundaries of his experience. Here, we have the body as poem: as Lemon so beautifully describes, "Melodies drill deep wells in the chest." —*Cate Marvin*

The City Is a Riding Tide, *a novel by Rebecca Lee* (Simon & Schuster): Fixed on a pair of Manhattan nonprofit workers who want to build an ill-fated healing center on a perilous bank of the Yangtze River, this is an urgent story infused with lyricism and populated by flawed people who both use one another and also sometimes try to do some good. Every sentence is unpredictable, challenging, and surprising, which can also be said of the turns in the plot, played out in the past and the present, in China, Canada, and New York, and alternately comic and tragic. Even a minor character stands accused of having "his own PR reasons, and actually, more insidiously than that, his own internal PR, the things he broadcast about himself to himself." —*Fred Leebron*

Journey to the Beach of the Dead, *poems by Richard Blanco* (Arizona): The speaker of Richard Blanco's second book serves as both tourist and guide to the reader throughout the relentless and far-flung journeying the poems undertake. Moving from otherness to origin, Blanco pulls away from such locales as Italy and Guatemala to reenter his own history as a Cuban-American boy growing up in Miami by recalling, with great tenderness, the antics of his stubborn and quite humorous *abuela,* among other family members. Despite his wide-varying subject matter, this is essentially a book of love poems: the speaker's observations, while so often movingly nostalgic, are always wise enough to ring true. —*Cate Marvin*

*Books Recommended by
Our Advisory Editors*

Madeline DeFrees recommends *Dark Alphabet,* poems by Jennifer Maier: "Jennifer Maier's colloquial language settles you comfortably into the passenger seat for a journey full of surprising turns. The poems are triggered by ordinary events: a friend's asking why she doesn't write novels; the sight of ducks in mating season. This first collection is a sophisticated blend of wit, intellect, feeling, and perception as mysterious as nightfall and as fresh as daybreak." (Southern Illinois)

Maxine Kumin recommends *Waking Stone,* poems by Carole Simmons Oles: "This creative biography-in-verse, about the life of a nineteenth-century sculptor who proved that a woman could handle a chisel as well as a palette, is often in the voice of Hosmer herself, and is lively, informative, and vividly told." (Arkansas)

Philip Levine recommends *The Ghost of You and Me,* poems by Wesley McNair: "I wonder if Maine is half as interesting as the poetry Wesley McNair has written about the place. He finds so many skewed and irresistible characters who manage to get into odd situations for which there is only one remedy: to persevere. In this new collection he strikes me as one of the great storytellers of contemporary poetry, a poetry which has largely given up narratives, perhaps because they require people other than the poet or in addition to the poet, a challenging task for solipsists ... Never before have I found McNair's brand of humor so subtle and af-firming. Nor when he wanders from his tales can I recall him writing such perfect small lyrics about damn near anything." (Godine)

Thomas Lux recommends *The Seed Thieves,* poems by Robert Fanning: "Robert Fanning is a powerful and urgent young poet whose work I have been following for some time. This, his first full-length collection, is a stunner." (Marick)

Gerald Stern recommends *Against Which,* poems by Ross Gay: "Ross Gay's *Against Which* is stunningly original, confrontational, and lovely. He reminds me of Hart Crane." (Cavan-Kerry)

*New Books by
Our Advisory Editors*

Martín Espada, *The Republic of Poetry,* poems: The republic in Espada's eighth collection is a glorious place of odes and elegies, memory and history, miracles and justice. (Norton)

Richard Ford, *The Lay of the Land,* a novel: In this triumphant follow-up to *Independence Day,* Frank Bascombe returns, acutely in thrall, as always, to life's endless complexities. (Knopf)

Mary Gordon, *The Stories of Mary Gordon,* stories: These forty-one pieces, half of which are new or have never been collected, masterfully capture the nuances of modern life. (Pantheon)

Marilyn Hacker, *Essays on Departure,* poems: This book gathers twenty-five years of elegant, delectable work from eight books, as well as translations and new poems. (Carcanet)

Yusef Komunyakaa, *Gilgamesh,* verse play: With playwright Chad Garcia, Komunyakaa has refashioned a classic Sumerian legend into a vibrant and compelling verse play. (Wesleyan)

Maxine Kumin, *Mites to Mastodons,* children's poems: A fascinating cornucopia of poems that exudes whimsical affection for all the creatures in our kingdom. Illustrated by Pamela Zagarenski. (Houghton Mifflin)

Paul Muldoon, *Horse Latitudes,* poems: This magnificent new collection presents us with fields of battle and fields of debate in which we often seem to be at a standstill. (FSG)

Mark Strand, *Man and Camel,* poems: Strand's remarkable eleventh collection is a toast to life's transience, abiding beauty, and the meaning in the sound of language. (Knopf)

CONTRIBUTORS' NOTES

ANNE ATIK's two books of poems are *Words in Hock* (1974) and *Offshore* (1991), both from Enitharmon Press. She also authored the memoir *How It Was*, about her friendship with Samuel Beckett. Other work has appeared in *APR, The Partisan Review, Literary Imagination, Pequod,* and *The Nation,* among others.

AMY BEEDER's first book is *Burn the Field* (Carnegie Mellon, 2006). She received a "Discovery"/*The Nation* Award in 2001, and her poems have appeared in *Poetry, Agni, Poetry Daily, The Nation, Pleiades, American Letters & Commentary,* and elsewhere. She teaches poetry at the University of New Mexico.

JOHN BENSKO's books of poetry include *Green Soldiers* (Yale), *The Waterman's Children* (Massachusetts), and *The Iron City* (Illinois). *Sea Dogs,* a collection of stories, was published by Graywolf Press. He teaches in the M.F.A. program at the University of Memphis.

FRANK BIDART's most recent book of poems is *Star Dust* (FSG, 2005). He also co-edited Robert Lowell's *Collected Poems.*

MICHAEL BORICH has an M.F.A. in Writing from the University of California–Irvine and is the author of two novels and a poetry collection, *The Black Hawk Songs* (Illinois). He is a professor of English at Qingdao University in the People's Republic of China.

J. BOYER teaches in the creative writing program at Arizona State University.

PEG BOYERS is Executive Editor of *Salmagundi* and author of a book of poems, *Hard Bread.* Her second book of poems, *Honey with Tobacco,* will be published by the University of Chicago Press in March 2007.

JOHN CASEY is the author of five books of fiction, two translations from Italian, and numerous essays and stories. His novel *Spartina* won the National Book Award. "Rapunzel" is one of the Rhode Island stories to be included in a trilogy, of which *Spartina* is the centerpiece.

JOHN CASTEEN is a designer and builder of custom furniture. He also teaches fiction, nonfiction, and poetry workshops through University of Virginia's School of Continuing Education, and serves on the editorial staff of *The Virginia Quarterly Review.* His work has appeared recently in *The Iowa Review, Shenandoah,* and *Meridian.*

CLARE CAVANAGH is the Herman and Beulah Pearce Miller Research Professor in Literature at Northwestern University. She is currently working on two books,

Poetry and Power: Russia, Poland, and the West (Yale) and *Czeslaw Milosz and His Age: A Critical Life* (FSG).

DAN CHIASSON is the author of two books of poetry, *The Afterlife of Objects* (Chicago, 2002) and *Natural History* (Knopf, 2005), and a book of criticism, *One Kind of Everything: Poem and Person in Contemporary America*. He teaches at Wellesley College.

HENRI COLE's fifth collection, *Middle Earth,* was a finalist for the Pulitzer Prize in Poetry. His new book, *Blackbird and Wolf,* will be published by Farrar, Straus & Giroux in April.

PETER COOLEY's books include *The Company of Strangers, The Room Where Summer Ends, Nightseasons, The Van Gogh Notebook, The Astonished Hours, Sacred Conversations,* and *A Place Made of Starlight.* He is a professor of English at Tulane University.

STEVEN CRAMER's fourth collection, *Goodbye to the Orchard* (Sarabande, 2004), won the New England Poetry Club's Sheila Motton Award, and was named a 2005 Honor Book in Poetry by the Massachusetts Center for the Book. He directs the low-residency M.F.A. program in creative writing at Lesley University.

STEPHEN CUSHMAN has published three volumes of poetry: *Blue Pajamas* (1998), *Cussing Lesson* (2002), and *Heart Island* (2006). He teaches at the University of Virginia, where he is Robert C. Taylor Professor of English.

W. S. DI PIERO's *Chinese Apples: New and Selected Poems* will appear from Knopf in early 2007. He writes frequently about the visual arts and lives in San Francisco.

BRYAN D. DIETRICH has won *The Paris Review* Poetry Prize, the "Discovery"/*The Nation* Award, and a Writers at Work Fellowship. His poetry has appeared in *Harvard Review, The Yale Review, Shenandoah, Prairie Schooner,* and many other journals. Author of two books, *Krypton Nights* (2002) and *Universal Monsters* (2007), he teaches at Newman University in Wichita, Kansas.

MAGGIE DIETZ is a lecturer in creative writing at Boston University and assistant poetry editor for *Slate.* Her awards include fellowships from the Fine Arts Work Center, Phillips Exeter Academy, and the New Hampshire State Arts Council. Her first book of poems is *Perennial Fall* (Chicago).

LANDIS EVERSON was born in 1926 in Coronado, California, and now lives in San Luis Obispo. His *Everything Preserved: Poems 1955–2005* (Graywolf, 2006) is the debut winner of the Emily Dickinson First Book Award from the Poetry Foundation. "Winter Park" is from a new collection in progress, *Book of Valentines.*

RICHARD FEIN's latest collections are *Mother Tongue* and *Reversion.* An earlier collection, *Kafka's Ear,* won the Maurice English Award. He has also published a memoir, *The Dance of Leah;* translations, *Selected Poems of Yankev Glatshteyn;* and a critical study, *Robert Lowell.* He lives in Cambridge, Massachusetts.

BRENDAN GALVIN's *Habitat: New and Selected Poems 1965–2005* was a finalist for the National Book Award. He lives in Truro, Massachusetts.

MEGAN GANNON graduated from Vassar College and the University of Montana. Her work is forthcoming in *Gulf Coast, Third Coast, Pleiades,* and *The Best American Poetry 2006.* She and her husband, the poet Miles Waggener, are newly Nebraskans.

LINDA GREGERSON's new book of poems, *Magnetic North,* will be published by Houghton Mifflin this coming March. She teaches poetry and Renaissance literature at the University of Michigan.

JANIS HALLOWELL is the author of *The Annunciation of Francesca Dunn* (2004). Her second novel will be published by William Morrow in 2008. A faculty member at the Lighthouse Writers Workshop, she has received support from the MacDowell Colony, Colorado Endowment for the Humanities, the Boulder Arts Commission, and the Rocky Mountain Women's Institute.

JEFF HARDIN teaches at Columbia State Community College in Columbia, Tennessee. His first collection, *Fall Sanctuary,* received the 2004 Nicholas Roerich Prize from Story Line Press. Recent and forthcoming poems appear in *Mid-American Review, Zone 3, Puerto del Sol, Smartish Pace, Poem, Potomac Review, The Café Review,* and others.

JEFFREY HARRISON's fourth book of poems, *Incomplete Knowledge,* was published by Four Way Books in November 2006. In addition, The Waywiser Press brought out *The Names of Things: New and Selected Poems* in England last June. His chapbook, *An Undertaking* (2005), is available on Amazon.com.

TODD HEARON's recent poems and articles appear in *Poetry, Slate, Parnassus,* and *Harvard Review.* He lives in Exeter, New Hampshire.

SCOTT HIGHTOWER's third book, *Part of the Bargain,* received Copper Canyon Press's 2004 Hayden Carruth Award. He lives and works in New York City.

BRENDA HILLMAN has written seven collections of poetry, all published by Wesleyan University Press, the most recent of which is *Pieces of Air in the Epic.* She teaches at Saint Mary's College in Moraga, California.

JANE HIRSHFIELD's most recent book is *After* (HarperCollins, 2006). She is the recipient of fellowships from the Academy of American Poets, the NEA, and the Guggenheim and Rockefeller foundations, and her work has appeared in multiple editions of both *The Best American Poetry* and *The Pushcart Prize* anthologies.

MICHAEL HOFMANN edited the anthology *20th Century German Poetry,* published by Farrar, Straus & Giroux in November. He is the author of several books of poems, and one of criticism.

TONY HOAGLAND won the 2005 Mark Twain Award from the Poetry Foundation. A book of craft essays, *Real Sofistikashun,* was released in October by Graywolf Press. He teaches at the University of Houston, and in the Warren Wilson M.F.A. program.

JOHN HOLLANDER's nineteenth book of poetry was *Picture Window*, published by Knopf in 2003, and he has most recently edited the *Selected Poetry of Emma Lazarus* and an anthology of *Poems Haunted and Bewitched*. He is Sterling Professor Emeritus of English at Yale.

FANNY HOWE's most recent publications include *The Lives of a Spirit, Glasstown: Where Something Got Broken* (Nightboat) and *On the Ground* (Graywolf). A collection of her novels, *Radical Love*, was released this fall.

SUSAN HOWE's most recent books are *The Midnight* (New Directions) and *Kidnapped* (Coracle). A CD called *Thiefth* (Blue Chopsticks), a collaboration with the musician/composer David Grubbs, has recently been released. She holds the Samuel P. Capen Chair in Poetry and the Humanities at the State University of New York at Buffalo.

COLETTE INEZ has published nine books of poetry and has won Guggenheim, Rockefeller, and two NEA fellowships and Pushcart Prizes. She teaches in Columbia University's Undergraduate Writing Program. Her memoir, *The Secret of M. Dulong*, has recently been released by the University of Wisconsin Press.

MARCIA KARP has poems and translations in *The Partisan Review, Republic of Letters, Literary Imagination, The Guardian, Seneca Review, Agenda, Harvard Review*, Penguin's *Catullus in English* and *Petrarch in English*, and forthcoming in the *TLS*.

MAURICE KILWEIN GUEVARA was born in Belencito, Colombia, and raised in Pittsburgh, Pennsylvania. His most recent book is *Autobiography of So-and-so: Poems in Prose*. He is a former president of AWP and currently a professor of English at the University of Wisconsin–Milwaukee.

JENNIFER L. KNOX's first book of poems, *A Gringo Like Me*, is from Soft Skull Press. She is a three-time contributor to *The Best American Poetry*, and her work has appeared in *Great American Prose Poems: From Poe to Present* and *Free Radicals: American Poets Before Their First Books*.

LAURIE LAMON is Associate Professor of English at Whitworth College in Spokane, Washington. Her poems have appeared in *The Atlantic Monthly, The New Republic, The New Criterion, Arts & Letters Journal of Contemporary Culture, Ploughshares*, and elsewhere. Her collection, *The Fork Without Hunger*, was published by CavanKerry Press.

RIKA LESSER is the author of three books of poems and the translator of many works of Swedish and German belles-lettres. "Possession," part of a series based on the works of the Swedish painter, sculptor, and graphic artist Lena Cronqvist, is from a new collection, *Questions of Love*.

JEFFREY LEVINE is the author of *Rumor of Cortez* (Red Hen, 2005), nominated for a 2006 *Los Angeles Times* Literary Award in Poetry, and *Mortal, Everlasting*, winner of the Transcontinental Poetry Prize from Pavement Saw Press (2002). He is Editor-in-Chief and Publisher of Tupelo Press, an independent literary press.

GAIL MAZUR's *Zeppo's First Wife: New & Selected Poems* (Chicago, 2005) won the Massachusetts Book Award and was a finalist for *The Los Angeles Times* Book Prize and the Paterson Poetry Prize. Her earlier books are *Nightfire, The Pose of Happiness, The Common,* and *They Can't Take That Away from Me,* a 2001 National Book Award finalist. She is Writer in Residence at Emerson College.

ASKOLD MELNYCZUK's new novel, *House of Widows,* will appear next year. His previous novels include a Best Book of 2002 from *The Los Angeles Times* and a Notable Book from *The New York Times.* Founding editor of *Agni,* he is currently publisher of Arrowsmith Books, and teaches at University of Massachusetts, Boston, and at Bennington College.

W. S. MERWIN's many awards include the 2005 National Book Award for *Migration: New and Selected Poems* (Copper Canyon), the Pulitzer Prize, the Tanning Prize, the Bollingen Award, and the Ruth Lilly Poetry Prize. He is the author of dozens of books of poetry and prose, most recently *Present Company* (Copper Canyon, 2005). For the past thirty years he has lived in Hawaii.

IDRA NOVEY's chapbook *The Next Country* was selected by Carolyn Forché for the 2005 Poetry Society of America Chapbook Fellowship. Her book of selected translations of Brazilian poet Paulo Henriques Britto received a PEN Translation Fund Award and is forthcoming from BOA Editions. She teaches writing at Columbia University.

ED OCHESTER's most recent book is *The Land of Cockaigne* (Story Line, 2001). Forthcoming is *Unreconstructed: Poems Selected and New* (Autumn House, 2007) and *American Poetry Now* (Pittsburgh, 2007), an anthology of contemporary American poetry. He edits the Pitt Poetry Series and the Drue Heinz Literature Prize, both from University of Pittsburgh Press, and co-edits the magazine *5 AM.*

LINDA PASTAN's twelfth book of poems, published in October 2006, is *Queen of a Rainy Country.* She received the 2003 Ruth Lilly Prize.

RICARDO PAU-LLOSA's sixth poetry title will be published by Carnegie Mellon, as were his last three books. He is also a widely published art critic. His website is www.pau-llosa.com.

ED PAVLIC's second book of poems, *Labors Lost Left Unfinished,* appeared in 2006 from Sheep Meadow Press. He is also the author of *Paraph of Bone & Other Kinds of Blue* (APR/Copper Canyon) and the critical book *Crossroads Modernism* (Minnesota, 2002). He directs the M.F.A./Ph.D. program in creative writing at The University of Georgia.

JOHN PECK's most recent books are *Collected Shorter Poems 1966–1996* (Northwestern, 2004) and *Red Strawberry Leaf: Selected Poems 1994–2001* (Chicago, 2005). He lives in southeastern Connecticut.

JOYCE PESEROFF's two new books are *Eastern Mountain Time* (Carnegie Mellon) and *Simply Lasting: Writers on Jane Kenyon* (Graywolf). She directs the creative writing program at University of Massachusetts, Boston, which will offer an M.F.A. degree beginning September 2007.

ROBERT PINSKY recently published *The Life of David,* a prose account of the Biblical figure, and a chapbook of poems, *First Things to Hand.* A new full-length collection, *Gulf Music,* will appear in fall 2007.

LIA PURPURA's new collection of essays, *On Looking,* has just been published by Sarabande Books. New poems are forthcoming in *The Southern Review, Tin House,* and elsewhere. She is Writer-in-Residence at Loyola College in Baltimore, Maryland. In spring 2007, she will be Bedell Visiting Writer in the Nonfiction Program at the University of Iowa.

MAURICE RIORDAN was born in County Cork, Ireland. *The Holy Land,* a new book of poems, will be published in the U.K. by Faber and Faber in February. He lives in London, where he teaches at Imperial College, and is editor of *Poetry London.*

J. ALLYN ROSSER's most recent book is *Misery Prefigured.* Last year she received the J. Howard and Barbara M. J. Wood Prize from *Poetry.* Her work has appeared recently in *Slate, The Georgia Review, The Atlantic Monthly, The Kenyon Review,* and *The Best American Poetry 2006.* She teaches at Ohio University.

MARK RUDMAN is the author of seven volumes of poetry and three of prose. He received the Max Hayward Award for his translation of Boris Pasternak's *My Sister—Life,* and he won the National Book Critics Circle Award for *Rider.* A section of his new book, the last of the *Rider* quintet, can be heard as a radio play on drunkenboat.com, with the actress Martha Plimpton in the role of the poet's mother.

TOMAŽ ŠALAMUN is widely recognized as one of the leading Central European poets and has had books translated into most of the European languages. He lives in Ljubljana and occasionally teaches in the United States. His recent books in English are *Blackboards* and *The Book for My Brother.*

SHEROD SANTOS is the author of five books of poetry, most recently *The Perishing* (2004). In 2005 he published *Greek Lyric Poetry: A New Translation.* In 1999 he received an Award for Literary Excellence from the American Academy of Arts and Letters.

AMY SCATTERGOOD has published one book of poetry, *The Grammar of Nails.* She lives with her two daughters in Los Angeles, where she teaches poetry at UCLA's Extension program and is a staff writer for the food section of *The Los Angeles Times.*

LLOYD SCHWARTZ is Frederick S. Troy Professor of English at The University of Massachusetts Boston, Classical Music Editor of *The Boston Phoenix,* and a regular commentator for NPR's *Fresh Air.* His most recent book of poems is *Cairo Traffic* (Chicago), and he is currently co-editing the collected works of Elizabeth Bishop for the Library of America.

DON SHARE is Poetry Editor of *Harvard Review* and Curator of the Poetry Room at Harvard University, where he teaches, and is now also Editor in Chief of *Literary Imagination.* His books include *Union; Seneca in English;* translations of

Miguel Hernández, *I Have Lots of Heart;* and the forthcoming critical edition *The Poems of Basil Bunting.*

HEDDI SIEBEL has received a Fulbright Scholar Award and a *National Geographic* Expeditions Council grant for a project in the Arctic Circle. Her prints and paintings are in private collections and the permanent collections of the Museum of Fine Arts, the DeCordova Museum, the Boston Public Library, and the Yale Art Gallery. She lives in Cambridge, Massachusetts.

ELIZABETH SPIRES, a past guest editor of *Ploughshares,* is the author of five collections of poetry, most recently *Now the Green Blade Rises* (Norton, 2002). Her books for children include *The Mouse of Amherst,* the tale of a small mouse who lives in Emily Dickinson's bedroom. She teaches at Goucher College in Baltimore.

MARK STRAND lives in New York and teaches at Columbia in the Department of English and Comparative Literature.

JULES SUPERVIELLE was born in Montevideo to French parents in 1884. He wrote prolifically during his lifetime, authoring twenty-nine volumes of poetry, and was admired by many of his contemporaries, including Valéry and Rilke. He died in 1960.

DEBORAH TALL has published four collections of poems, most recently *Summons.* Her latest book is *A Family of Strangers,* a memoir of secrecy and lost history in the form of a lyric essay, just out from Sarabande Books. She teaches at Hobart and William Smith Colleges, where she is editor of *Seneca Review.*

PIMONE TRIPLETT is the author of *The Price of Light* (Four Way Books, 2005) and *Ruining the Picture* (*TriQuarterly*/Northwestern, 1998). She holds an M.F.A. from the University of Iowa. Currently, she teaches at the University of Washington and the Warren Wilson M.F.A. Program for Writers.

KATE WALBERT is the author of a collection of stories, *Where She Went,* and the novels *The Gardens of Kyoto* and *Our Kind,* which was a finalist for the 2004 National Book Award. She lives in New York City with her family.

DAVID WEISS's first novel, *The Mensch,* came out in 1998. "Cry Baby" is the first section of a new novel of the same title. He is a poet whose work has recently appeared in *Literary Imagination* and *Narrative Theory.* He teaches at Hobart and William Smith Colleges.

CHARLES WRIGHT lives in Charlottesville, Virginia, and teaches at the University of Virginia. He is the author most recently of *Scar Tissue.* The poem in this issue is from a book-length sequence entitled *Littlefoot,* which is forthcoming in 2007.

FRANZ WRIGHT's *Walking to Martha's Vineyard* received the 2004 Pulitzer Prize in Poetry. His new collection is *God's Silence* (Knopf, 2006). He is currently the visiting poet-in-residence at Brandeis University.

ADAM ZAGAJEWSKI received the 2004 Neustadt Prize in Literature. His most recent volume, *Music I Have Heard with You*, translated by Clare Cavanagh, is forthcoming from Farrar, Straus & Giroux. He divides his time between Krakow and Houston, where he teaches in the writing program at the University of Houston.

∼

GUEST EDITOR POLICY *Ploughshares* is published three times a year: mixed issues of poetry and fiction in the Spring and Winter and a fiction issue in the Fall, with each guest-edited by a different writer of prominence, usually one whose early work was published in the journal. Guest editors are invited to solicit up to half of their issues, with the other half selected from unsolicited manuscripts screened for them by staff editors. This guest editor policy is designed to introduce readers to different literary circles and tastes, and to offer a fuller representation of the range and diversity of contemporary letters than would be possible with a single editorship. Yet, at the same time, we expect every issue to reflect our overall standards of literary excellence. We liken *Ploughshares* to a theater company: each issue might have a different guest editor and different writers—just as a play will have a different director, playwright, and cast—but subscribers can count on a governing aesthetic, a consistency in literary values and quality, that is uniquely our own.

∼

SUBMISSION POLICIES We welcome unsolicited manuscripts from August 1 to March 31 (postmark dates). All submissions sent from April to July are returned unread. In the past, guest editors often announced specific themes for issues, but we have revised our editorial policies and no longer restrict submissions to thematic topics. Submit your work at any time during our reading period; if a manuscript is not timely for one issue, it will be considered for another. We do not recommend trying to target specific guest editors. Our backlog is unpredictable, and staff editors ultimately have the responsibility of determining for which editor a work is most appropriate. Mail one prose piece or one to three poems. We do not accept e-mail submissions, but we now accept submissions online. Please see our website (www.pshares.org) for more information and specific guidelines. Poems should be individually typed either single- or double-spaced on one side of the page. Prose should be typed double-spaced on one side and be no longer than thirty pages. Although we look primarily for short stories, we occasionally publish personal essays/memoirs. Novel excerpts are acceptable if self-contained. Unsolicited book reviews and criticism are not considered. Please send only one manuscript at a time, either by mail or online. Do not send a second submission until you have heard about the first. *There is a limit of two submissions per reading period, regardless of genre, whether it is by mail or online.* Additional submissions will be returned unread. Mail your manuscript in a page-size manila envelope, your full name and address written on the outside. In general, address submissions to the "Fiction Editor," "Poetry Editor," or "Nonfiction Editor," not to the guest or staff editors by name, unless you have a legitimate association with them or have been previously published in the magazine. Unsolicited work sent directly to a guest editor's home or office will be ignored and discarded; guest editors are formally instructed not to read such work. *All mailed manuscripts and correspondence regarding submissions should be accompanied by a business-size, self-addressed, stamped envelope (s.a.s.e.) for a response only. Manuscript copies will be recycled, not returned.* No replies will be given by postcard or e-mail (exceptions are made for international submissions). Expect three to five months for a decision. We now receive well over a thousand manuscripts a month. Do not query us until five months have passed, and if you do, please write to us, including an s.a.s.e. and indicating the postmark date of submission, instead of calling or e-mailing. Simultaneous submissions are amenable as long as they are indicated as such and we are notified immediately upon acceptance elsewhere. We cannot accommodate revisions, changes of return address, or forgotten s.a.s.e.'s after the fact. We do not reprint previously published work. Translations are welcome if permission has been granted. We cannot be responsible for delay, loss, or damage. Payment is upon publication: $25/printed page, $50 minimum and $250 maximum per author, with two copies of the issue and a one-year subscription.

~

THE NAME *Ploughshares* **1.** The sharp edge of a plough that cuts a furrow in the earth. **2 a.** A variation of the name of the pub, the Plough and Stars, in Cambridge, Massachusetts, where the journal *Ploughshares* was founded in 1971. **2 b.** The pub's name was inspired by the Sean O'Casey play about the Easter Rising of the Irish "citizen army." The army's flag contained a plough, representing the things of the earth, hence practicality; and stars, the ideals by which the plough is steered. **3.** A shared, collaborative, community effort. **4.** A literary journal that has been energized by a desire for harmony, peace, and reform. Once, that spirit motivated civil rights marches, war protests, and student activism. Today, it still inspirits a desire for beating swords into ploughshares, but through the power and the beauty of the written word.

NATIONAL
ENDOWMENT
FOR THE ARTS

masscculturalcouncil.org

Ploughshares Donors

With great gratitude, we would like to acknowledge the following subscribers who generously made donations to *Ploughshares* during 2006.

Anonymous (17)
John M. Anderson
John W. Andrews
Helene Atwan
Geoffrey Becker
Barbara Blount
Jill Bossert
Henry Bromell
Alice Byers
Edward H. Cardoza, Jr.
Sylvia Cima-Erlbaum
Saralyn Daly
Susan Dewitt Davie
Mary Lynn H. Dickson
Douglas W. Downey
Paula Eder
Deb Farrow
Frederick A. Ficken
Steven Finkelstein
George Garrett
Teja Geldmacher
Katie Hammersly
Jeffrey Harrison
Joann Karges
Karen Katz
Lilian Kemp
X. J. Kennedy
Kristen R. Kish
Maxine Kumin
Barbara Kurle
James C. Lambert

David Leviten
Dr. Harold R. Lohr
Mary Luddy
Thomas Lux
Fred Marchant
B. Marsh
Delia Moon
Neil Mullin
Judith Pacht
Dr. Rod Parker
Patricia Polak
Alex Porter
Gerald and Patricia Raker
Liam Rector &
   Tree Swenson
Jennifer Rose
Marly Rusoff
Valerie Sayers
Philip Schultz
David L. Sherwood
Carol Houck Smith
Maura Stanton
Elizabeth H. Timmer
Philip Timpane
   Timpane Construction
Nigel Twose
Richard L. Vittitow
Margaret S. Voight
Margot Wizansky
Don Zancanella

PRAISE FOR **post road**

> "*Post Road*, from its inception, has been an exotic and intelligent literary treat. I always like to see what they come up with each issue, and they never fail to surprise, entertain, and enlighten."
>
> JONATHAN AMES

> "I always read *Post Road* with great enthusiasm. In its stealthy, unassuming way, it has become one of the most reliable and ambitious literary magazines in America."
>
> RICK MOODY

> "*Post Road* is one of the most interesting and exciting literary magazines out there. If you care about reading and writing, do yourself a favor and check it out."
>
> TOM PERROTTA

> "*Post Road* maps the way to the freshest and funkiest literary territories. As the group The Postal Service does for music, *Post Road* fuses eclectic elements into something whole and wholly new."
>
> ELIZABETH SEARLE

> "The editors' enthusiasm is palpable; they consistently provide a lively home for writing worth reading."
>
> AMY HEMPEL

> "Post Road has the goods. I not only fall on them and read them like hot news when they come in the door, I keep them lined up on my shelf like little books, because that's what they are."
>
> JONATHAM LETHEM

1 YEAR: $18, 2 YEARS: $34 **WWW.POSTROADMAG.COM**

ARTCRITICISMFICTIONNONFICTIONPOETRYTHEATREETCETERARECOMMENDATIONS

BENNINGTON WRITING SEMINARS

MFA in Writing and Literature
Two-Year Low-Residency Program

A. BLAKE GARDNER

FICTION
NONFICTION
POETRY